W. van der Marck?
Nijmegen (in USSR)
16-3-65

Books by Sidney Cohen

The Beyond Within

The Beyond Within

The LSD Story

BY *Sidney Cohen*, M.D.

FOREWORD BY DR. GARDNER MURPHY,
DIRECTOR OF RESEARCH, MENNINGER FOUNDATION

NEW YORK Atheneum 1964

Foreword

In this age of chemistry as the "central science" around which are ordered the worlds of the living and of the nonliving, there are many breakthroughs which startle even the most sophisticated. The impact upon the biological, as well as the biosocial, nature of man is already becoming so obvious and so vast that it is extraordinarily difficult to maintain perspective. One demands either too much or, quite often, too little.

One may then develop both deep gratitude and an earnest sense of intellectual companionship as one goes hand in hand with Dr. Sidney Cohen through this world of extraordinary new discoveries in the land of the impact of chemistry—specifically, of one powerful drug upon the psychological world of man. One cannot afford here to be starry-eyed and breathless in the face of great present and potential discoveries; one must remain sober and poised through every chapter on the way. One does need, however, the companionship of a solid and systematic investigator like Dr. Cohen, who has the patience and the objectivity to maintain perspective through the midst of such extraordinary phenomena. Here one encounters visions and remade phantasy worlds which must be carefully examined and compared with dozens of types of human experience, familiar and exceptional, to get a balanced picture as to what the nature of such experience may be; and one must then consider, in terms of history, anthropology, psychology, psychiatry, psychoanalysis, what the special symbolic meanings may be under certain circumstances or for certain people.

This unfolding is centered, of course, very largely in the first-hand reports under carefully described conditions of observation. It is important to see both what the psychiatrist sees, and also what the subject or patient sees at the time and as he remembers the experience. There must, in other words, be careful research protocols and systematic analyses both of the inner and of the outer worlds here conjoined in a systematic record. In an introductory book of this sort, the psychiatric observations and psychological test reports cannot be detailed, as would be appropriate in a technical report. The reader, however, who is sensitive to the words of subjects and the words of psychiatrists will realize that in a large proportion of the records, men and women were carried into a world of very great intensity, very great beauty, and very great challenge.

At the same time the reader will recognize that this is a world in which we must tread ever so lightly, with ever so wise a guide. We face a world of very great challenge, and also of very great potential danger if the guide is not adequate both to his scientific and to his personal sense of responsibility. This book will be of no comfort to those who believe that sublime and ego-shattering experience can easily be indulged in by all easy risk takers. The very fact that the experience is capable of giving intense visions and intense new awareness, or conviction of awareness, of one's fellows and one's place in the universe does not in itself "prove" anything about the sources or the ultimate meanings of the experience. It will, however, profoundly interest those who have a deep concern with the broadening of human consciousness. It is a book at a scientific level which is, at the same time, a book stretching the imagination as to what this new world of chemistry may bring us.

GARDNER MURPHY

Introduction

This is a book about a controversial, even taboo, subject. It deals with a group of drugs which affect the mind and affect it profoundly. Some people say that these drugs disorganize and disrupt mental activity, others feel that they organize and integrate the mind. Some call the drugs hallucinogens and claim they produce a temporary madness, others call them psychedelics and assert that they induce valuable states of self-transcendence and mystical unity. These differences are part of the controversy.

The contingency that one day thought control with drugs will be practiced is a chilling one—so disturbing that our emotions obscure whatever data are available for a reasoned appraisal of the possibility. In a matter of this sort neutrality does not exist, only varying degrees of prejudice or a simple refusal to face the issue. The hallucinogens are deeply involved in the problem of possible thought control. Other basic issues cluster around these drugs: how beliefs and value systems are acquired, whether drugs should be used to change consciousness, the relationship between the visionary and the schizophrenic state.

But what appear to be opposites are joined below the surface—and by a chemical. The contrasts extend into such other areas as why one person can experience insanity and another transcendent bliss from the same potion and why a chemical warfare agent can have relevance to psychotherapy. How is this possible? The debaters on these subjects never quite make contact, they speak different languages, and fluent translators have not yet come forth. It is a bit like the fable of the four blind men trying to describe an elephant, each in turn giving precise information on tail, leg, trunk and ear, insisting the others are wrong. Research is plagued with this sort of bias because it deliberately sets out to study tiny pieces of big problems. The difficulties are compounded in evaluating the LSD state, for it is extremely variable, highly subjective and hard to measure. Its elephantine dimension remains obscure, and the blind scoff at the blind.

Although the focus of this book is on LSD and the other hallucinogens, what emerges from a decade of study of these drugs is an enhanced appreciation of the vastness of the mind—the interminable, intricate interplay of seeing, thinking and feeling—the incredible immensity of that submerged continent, the unconscious. There is a vast beyond that lies within.

Drugs like LSD reveal something of the otherwise dimly visible expanse of the mind and suggest that its vast potential is scarcely to be comprehended. Why our species should have evolved such a remarkable instrument becomes a very pertinent question.

The brain is an underpowered (20 watts, according to Kety) self-scrutinizing symbol factory whose main job is body management. Its side line consists of reflecting on what it is, where it is going and what it all means. Its unique capacities for wonder and self-awareness are quite unnecessary for purposes of physical survival. If these emerging qualities of the human mind have a purpose, it can hardly be discerned from our present psychological position. The possibility that these attributes represent random by-products of an increasingly complex nervous system might be entertained. That consciousness and self-awareness are neither accidental nor incidental activities is much more likely. Over the millennia the forebrain, the locus of these operations, has grown more rapidly than has the rest of the cerebrum, and this differential rate of growth seems likely to continue.

The brain is an almost unspoiled wilderness; its exploration and charting have just begun. The voyagers of the past did little more than give quaint names to its protuberances. The better-equipped surveyors of this century have begun to penetrate into the limitless expanses. With the more effective instrumentation of our era, penetrations into the matted jungle have been made. Some of the reports from these expeditions will be noted in the following chapters.

No one yet knows the limits of his mind. Even the momentary glimpses discerned spontaneously or with LSD are fragmentary indeed. If we were to extrapolate from these bits, it could easily be said that our potential is never closely approached, and the mind ordinarily functions at a fraction of its full effectiveness. The promise of the future is that we will learn how to alter the fraction to our advantage.

Contents

The Beyond Within

1 Preview

"What is it really like? What happens to ordinary people when they take a drug like LSD?"

My answer to questions of this sort is a helpless silence. I remember the wide difference in our subjects' reactions, and their difficulty in expressing what was happening to them. They generally agreed that words were not the right medium to try a description of the LSD state. One of the more frustrated asked, "How do you describe red to a person who was born blind?"

Still, since this book is devoted to an understanding of the LSD condition and a consideration of its implications, the effort must be made. Reports from a number of people will be used in an effort to view the LSD state from a variety of positions. Hopefully, some approximation of its dimensions will result.

To a congenitally blind man who wants to know what color is like I would say: "Remember, if you are ever to understand what red is like you must open your mind to it. Do not say that it does not exist simply because you have never experienced it. I shall do what I can, but redness cannot be made into words. It is as different from words as ice is from vapor."

To you I would say: "The words in this book are as different from the LSD state as ice is from vapor."

To offer a foretaste of the varieties of LSD experience I have selected two narrative reports. One is from a young man who came into the laboratory, was checked over, and in due time was given LSD. He was just one of a series of subjects, nothing extraordinary about him. His reason for volunteering to take the drug? He was a psychology student, had heard about the visual effects, and thought it would be interesting to see what they were like.

This is part of a letter written that same evening:

My dearest darling Ruth:

The strangest thing happened on the way to me this day. I met myself and found that I'm really not me after all. Or perhaps I should say that I have found out what it is like to exist. For that's all there was left that instant, at that instant when feeling, thinking, being, all were caught up into one ebbing unity; a unity which was me, but not me, too. A me-not me which stood there nakedly and pointed back at itself in a sorrowful joy, and asked "Why?" That's all, just "Why?" But then the "why" didn't matter and it just *was!* I have now the strangest feeling that I'm so alone and yet so crowded. Have you ever felt like all that existed was you, and that suddenly the reason for your "youness" was knocked out from underneath you?

5

For today that me-watcher became the watched and
the watcher became un-me. How can all this come out
of one little capsule of LSD? Or perhaps, I should ask,
where was all this before now? I can't imagine all of
this "me" being bottled up and kept away from me. I
have the strangest feeling that I'm slightly (?) crazy, but
for some reason it doesn't really matter, since that's the
way it must be. Ruth, darling, how do I tell you about
the first time I didn't feel alone in my little shell? For
once my aloneness was overcome.

 . . . The last of the long-desired "visual-effects" are
now wearing off, the last of the numbness, the last of
the gnawing pain in my stomach. But yet something
remains behind; it has left something—I guess you
might say a footprint, in the eternity which has come
into existence since it first began to wreak its little havoc
of hell and heaven, of orgasm and pain, and fear and
hope, and beauty and filth. Ruth, I can't explain what
it was like. I remember saying, "It's too much for me,
it's too much." Was I afraid! I felt like a little boy, a
naked, bare-faced little boy. And I pleaded, "Please
stop, I don't want to see me." But it came anyway; and
it overwhelmed me like the ocean washing over a little
boy's sand castle despite the little dikes and moats. It
washed over the little sand castle me and spread my sands
over the ocean floor of existence and said: "Now go find
yourself and live like before." To lose that ever-present
feeling of being yourself, yourself as separate from
everything else, and to let go to the overpowering flood
of emotion, feeling, loving, hating, being *together with
everything else* . . . that's where the newness comes

in. I'm afraid my little old ego will never be the same. It can't be; it couldn't be; it mustn't.

Perhaps all of this sounds like hog-wash and drivel, or perhaps like the psychotic ramblings of a schizophrenic, or the hallucinations of paranoia. I don't know; but I do know that from now on I'm going to feel a little different about the kind of language we use to describe psychotics and their "little worlds." I'm going to watch a little closer and see if maybe what they are trying to describe isn't something like what I feel now and what I felt like then. I'm going to look a little closer at what the mystics are trying to tell us; at what the philosophers have to say about this. What I'm trying to say is that I think there's a lot to this that isn't a one-time thing. I think others feel the same way, with or without the damned drug, and I think maybe they've struggled with what to do with it all and what to make out of it all and maybe they can help me. I feel like a little boy— helpless but yet with a feeling of all-powerfulness and all-pervasiveness. Maybe Freud's description of primary narcissism is close to what I feel and felt. Maybe today the process of 22 years was suddenly reversed by this little drug called LSD. Maybe. Is that what it is? . . .

I have just come back from seeing the world for the first time. A little over two hours ago by watch time I went out to eat dinner, and I'll be damned if life isn't beautiful. I sat in the restaurant just enjoying living. Everything seemed so clear and beautiful. It was like looking at the world for the very, very first time and thinking to yourself, how beautiful, how sensuous! ! The people in the restaurant must really have thought me queer. I watched the ice in the ice water, the water on the counter top, the reflection of the ceiling in the water, I watched the waitresses, the busboys, and above all else, I watched the cheese melt on top of my hamburger. Have you ever watched the foam on a glass of beer? What a world of delight can exist in such a common thing. I looked at the people sitting around, all grouchy and grumpy, and felt sorry for them. Can't they see how beautiful life is? . . . I remember looking down the street and thinking to myself how many lights there are in the city and nobody to look at them. I think that I'm coming back to being myself now, whatever that means, but I hope that some of the joy which I have felt in just existing can stay with me and help me through the humdrum world which I fear I am going to fall back into shortly. Funny, but all the time while I was walking around on the streets and seeing, I was thinking about when I said that all this was "too much." I remember now that I said, or felt, "It's too much for me, I'm just a kid." But as I walked and looked at the sky, at the trees, at the shadows, the cars, the lights, just everything, I suddenly realized what I had meant by saying it's too much. I had the wrong slant on it. The world looked to me like it must to a little child, all big and beautiful. And I was experiencing it without the imposed controls that we have to slap on the world in order to become adults. I think I was afraid that my hold on the difference between the child's and adult's world wasn't too firm—and all those sights were just too overwhelming. As I was out walking I was, literally, experiencing the world as a child would, and I loved it and didn't give a damn about what anybody thought. I was almost drunk with rapture and I felt like bursting. I think that now I notice the physical boundaries of my body coming back and the same thing is happening to my mind. But does it have to be this way? Do we have to live alone? There must be something else than going back. I don't really want to "integrate" this thing into my ego and go back. But, I suddenly realize how tired I am. I am extremely tired, like my body and mind have been a battleground. I think I shall sleep well tonight.

I think that I'm going to quit typing now and lie down, I think my back is very sore. So, darling, I hope you didn't mind too much sharing this little bit of time with me, and maybe getting a glimpse of what I have been through, felt, become, what all, in this last twelve hours. Undoubtedly we'll have many chances to sit down and laugh about it in the future, I hope there is a future for us, but I hope we don't laugh too much, but then, I hope we don't cry. Like I said, "A funny thing happened" . . .

———

A moving letter from an ordinary guy. It was written to his girl friend, but with a copy to us to comply with our requirement for a report. He had expected the highly touted "visual effects," not the enormous changes of identity and meaning.

What happens after such an encounter? Is it therapeutic? Does it fade away like a dream? An attempt to answer these questions will be made in the pages to follow.

9

But before we go on with the story, the extreme range of LSD effects ought to be brought out by extracting from the narration of another psychologist whose response was neither pleasant nor enlightening.

. . . Over my right shoulder I could vaguely see what looked like a winged animal. It reminded me of a pterodactyl and it frightened me considerably. I was quite scared of it. We went on with the test though I still felt somewhat terrified of this thing. It seemed that instead of being in the room, it shifted outside as if I was too scared to have it inside with me and I put it outside. I felt often that it was beating its wings out there trying to get in. I could see through the window the flickering shadow of it. And once or twice I heard its wings. I was so terrified by this thing that I just couldn't move. Another peculiar reaction was that every time I heard this thing, the tester would turn a pale green color and his face would assume the consistency of cream cheese with his eyebrows and hair being very finely etched against his pale face. It was the most frightening experience I've ever had.

Now let's start at the beginning.

2 *The Search*

A pervasive drive that is singularly human is the need to temporarily change our state of awareness, to alter private reality, to be beside ourselves for a while. We are the only species that experiences this need; somehow the ordinary range of consciousness is incompletely satisfying to us.

Many techniques are available to accomplish some sort of consciousness alteration, including the use of a wide variety of drugs. In the West we are most familiar with the anesthetic alcohol—both with its initial stage of excitation and with the subsequent clouded, depressive phases. In the Orient opium, a narcotic, is favored. Both drugs now have a global distribution, with alcohol outdistancing opium and its derivatives. In a way the two are rather unfortunate choices. Alcohol can call forth a pleasant reduction of tension and discomfort, but unless the dose is carefully measured, a dulling stupor or social disinhibition ensues. Opium, except in extraordinary individuals like DeQuincey, invokes a torpid inertia. Both are addicting and may culminate in serious social, economic and physical depletion. A momentary phase of dilated awareness and intensified perception may occur with the distillates of the grape and the poppy, but it is all too transient and is lost in the somnolence that intervenes. Sedatives such as the barbiturates, the tranquilizers and the hypnotics are also well known and widely used to provide tension reduction, calming, forgetfulness or oblivion.

Sometimes an enhanced alertness or heightened contact with the environment is preferred. Then, stimulants or energizers—such as tea, coffee, khat, benzedrine, pituri or cocaine are taken, according to one's locale.

Almost any drug, if ingested in sufficient quantities by a person sensitive to its effects, can produce a delirium. This is a confusional state marked by disorientation, delusional thinking and hallucinations. Certain medicaments exist which can cause delirium in more than a few people. They belong to a variety of categories from the flavoring agent nutmeg to the antispasmodic belladonna, including the volatile solvents in airplane glue and common weeds like henbane, loco weed and the May apple. Alcohol, of course, when imbibed in prodigious quantities over long periods of time can culminate in the delirium tremens, the delirial pattern most frequently seen in our culture.

Delirium, sedation or stimulation are not quite the states with which we are here concerned. Other, more interesting, dimensions of awareness are possible, ranging from the profoundest feelings of mystical union to terrifying convictions of madness and from ecstasy to

despair. Drugs which mediate these disparate phenomena naturally have many names; they are generically
called hallucinogens, producers of hallucinations. This
is a rather poor designation because true hallucinations
are rarely encountered. But an hallucination is such a
striking event that it has lent its name to the experience.
What is more impressive, after all, than actually seeing
a thing which is not there?

These drugs might be called "pseudohallucinogens"
with more accuracy, but this is an awkward conglomer-
ate of a word. A pseudohallucination is perceived but is
evaluated as fictitious. "Illusinogen" is an even more
precise designation, but probably will never be adopted.
An illusion is an error in seeing based upon some
sensory cue—for example, a crack on the wall which is
identified as a snake. Most of the LSD visual phenomena
are illusions, the elaboration of something "out there"
into a misperception.

"Psychotomimetic," a mimicker of psychosis, is the
word most often found in the scientific literature. When
these drugs came under scientific scrutiny after World
War II, they were believed to cause a "model psychosis,"
a "madness in miniature." The hope was that a
schizophrenia-producing drug might teach us how to
cure psychiatry's greatest problem in the laboratory. It is
now generally agreed that the drugged state does not
quite mimic the naturally occurring schizophrenias.
"Mysticomimetic" is another designation, which calls
attention to the mystical states that can be duplicated.

"Psychotomimetic" describes only one aspect of the
LSD state. Most people who take the drug do not

become psychotic. Perhaps a very appropriate name for the gamut of possible response forms would be "psychotomystic," a malapropism borrowed from the report of one of our subjects.

The German name given by Lewin was "fantastica" and they certainly are fantastic. Osmond suggested "psychedelic," mind-manifesting, because he felt that a non-judgmental name might avoid stereotyped thinking about the unique states of consciousness which were induced. We shall use these names interchangeably giving preference to "hallucinogen" because it is in common usage.

This is by no means a new group of pharmacologic agents. Almost every subculture has sought out some root, herb or berry to induce dissociation (a selective change in consciousness so that ordinary waking awareness is markedly altered). When natural aids could not be found locally, strenuous physical means were developed. The Egyptians, for example, practiced a combination of sensory deprivation, fasting and social isolation in their ancient temple rites. Heat, thirst and the burning sun produced a sort of crude delirium in the participants of the Sun ritual of the Sioux. The physical contortions and breathing exercises of the yoga techniques practiced by Brahmanism and Buddhism and the rapid circling rhythms, long abstinent vigils and the breath retentions of the Sufis were a part of the search for dissociation.

The methods of the Greeks at Delphi were more sophisticated. In order to invoke the Gift of Prophecy, an old woman, known as the Pythoness, was attired as a maiden. She drank from the underground stream called Kawsotis. Whether the waters contributed to her ability to procure divinatory powers is unknown. What certainly helped was seating her upon a tripod placed over a fissure in the rock from which carbon dioxide gas emanated. This may have induced the seizurelike trance and the subsequent act of divination, since high concentrations of carbon dioxide are quite capable of changing consciousness. Whenever the gas vent gave out, sacred laurel leaves were scorched in a hot copper bowl and inhaled. These fumes likewise contained carbon dioxide. In nearby Eleusis a vision-inducing mushroom might have been employed—at any rate the Eleusian mystery involved "ineffable visions."

Of the hallucinogens, the most ancient is *soma pulari*. This is the legendary Persian potion which, according to the Sanskrit chronicle "made one like a God." What is called soma today, *sarcostema viminalis,* is incapable of even approximating such a condition. Either its potency has failed through the ages or its identity was confused with another plant.

Another "banisher of sorrow" has also been lost to modern psychobotany. This is nepenthe, which Homer refers to in the *Odyssey* on the occasion of Telemachus' visit to Menelaus in the course of his search for his father, Odysseus. Helen, Menelaus' wife, formerly of Troy, prepared the potion:

"Then Helen, daughter of Zeus, turned to new thoughts. Presently, she cast a drug into the wine whereof they drank, a drug to lull all pain and anger, and bring forgetfulness of every sorrow. Whoso should drink a draught thereof, when it is mingled in the bowl, on that day he would let no tear fall down his cheeks, not though his mother and his father died, not though men slew his brother or dear son with the sword before his face and his own eyes beheld it. Medicines of such virtue and so helpful had the daughter of Zeus, which Polydamna, the wife of Thor, had given her, a woman of Egypt, where earth, the grain-giver, yields herbs in greatest plenty, many that are healing in the cup, and many baneful." This was nepenthe.

Hashish (*cannabis indica,* Indian hemp, marihuana) has been consumed in India and Egypt since time immemorial. It has a strange, varied, and fascinating history. Yogis and other contemplatives took it to still the distractions and to attend to their thoughts in an egoless trance. On the other hand it was the glorious reward of the Thugs and Hashishans (assassins) when their business of knifing or garroting had been successfully completed. According to Herodotus, the Scythians who inhabited what is now the Soviet Union customarily threw hemp seeds onto hot stones and inhaled the vapors. Hashish is well known from the bazaars of Bengal to Tangiers and in most other parts of the world. By far its weirdest application is in the Dugpas Tibetan *momea.* This is a brew of the resin from the flowering tops of Indian hemp emulsified into warm human fat and served in a chalice made from a man's skull.

In Western cities the marginally adjusted smoke marihuana either for "kicks" or to work up enough courage to commit a felony.

This broad diversity of effects upon different individuals when taken for divergent purposes is not an exceptional phenomenon. It is an intrinsic part of the way these particular drugs affect mental function and will be considered at length later. Some 300 million people are supposed to use hashish regularly, almost as many as those who take opium.

The deadly *Amanita muscarina,* the fly agaric, is a crimson spotted mushroom reproduced by Walt Disney in his "Fantasia." Its name derives from the custom of generations of German hausfraus who crumbled it into saucers of water and set it out on a window sill to kill flics. This was not its sole use, however. It has been nibbled by tribesmen along the northern tier of the Eurasian land mass. On the dreary Kamchatkan peninsula, Koryak nomads discovered that when they partook of a measured amount of the colorful mushroom, a brilliant, glowing world of fantasy was theirs for a few hours. How they came to find that the urine of the amanita eater was likewise hallucinogenic is unknown, but this practice has been attested to by travelers from Oliver Goldsmith on. The excretory economics of the mushroom are such that up to five can benefit from the mushroom eating of a single amanita eater if they sip the voided liquid serially. (Urine drinking, by the way, is not a socially repugnant practice in many parts of the world. In wide areas of the Southern Sahara, cattle and human urine is quaffed, not for dreams, but for its salt content.)

The Siberian tribesman enjoyed his amanita reverie while beating out a rhythm seated on the dirt floor of his makeshift hut. Not so the bearskin-clad Scandinavian who, prior to battle, is supposed to have chewed fly agaric and gone "berserk." His courage was flawless and his strength so superhuman that the persecuted medieval Christian had a prayer attesting to it: "From the intolerable fury of the Norseman, oh Lord, deliver us." Fabing believes that the berserker chemically induced a ferocious rage with amanita, and he cites many students of tenth-century Scandinavian lore to prove the theory. Was it a racial character difference which caused the Norseman to be infuriated while the Kamchatkan was pacified by the same drug? Or was it due to a difference in the purpose for which the amanita mushroom was taken?

Another genus of mushroom, the psilocybe of southern Mexico, is a much safer and more effective hallucinogen. Long before the Aztec civilization flourished it was an important part of the religious rites. Not without reason was it called *teonanacatl*, "God's flesh," or "the divine mushroom." Hundreds of stone mushroom figurines in Mexico and Guatemala remain to attest to the reverence in which these fungi were held by the Indians. Ten years ago in Oaxaca, the Wassons rediscovered the cult. In the curandera's (the local priestess) darkened hut, in the stillness of the night broken only by her chant, they participated in a "soul-shattering" ceremony. In a later expedition the Wassons were accompanied by R. Heim, an expert mycologist, who was able to identify and classify the mushrooms used by the Indians in their ceremonies. Later he grew cultures of some of the species in his laboratory in Paris. He sent some of the cultivated material to Hofmann in Basle who tried it on a variety of animals without being able to observe any distinct effect. In order to determine whether the artificially grown specimens were potent, he ate thirty-two mushrooms and proceeded to have an experience familiar to him from an earlier exposure to LSD:

Thirty minutes after taking the mushrooms the exterior world began to undergo a strange transformation. Everything assumed a Mexican character. As I was perfectly well aware that my knowledge of the Mexican origin of the mushrooms would lead me to imagine only Mexican scenery, I tried deliberately to look on my environment as I knew it normally. But all voluntary efforts to look at things in their customary forms and colors proved ineffective. Whether my eyes were closed or open, I saw only Mexican motifs and colors. When the doctor supervising the experiment bent over me to check my blood pressure, he was transformed into an Aztec priest, and I would not have been astonished if he had drawn an obsidian knife. In spite of the seriousness of the situation, it amused me to see how the Germanic face of my colleague had acquired a purely Indian expression. At the peak of the intoxication, about one and one-half hours after ingestion of the mushrooms, the rush of interior pictures, mostly abstract motifs rapidly changing in shape and color, reached such an alarming degree that I feared that I would be pulled into this whirlpool of form and color and would dissolve. After about six hours the dream came to an end. Subjectively, I had no idea how long this condition had lasted. I felt my return to everyday reality to be a happy return into an old and familiar world from a strange, fantastic, but quite really experienced one.

Mexico is particularly blessed (or cursed) with plants that fabricate waking dreams. Two varieties of seeds of ololiuqui, the wild tropical American morning glory (*Rivea corymbosa* and *Ipomoea violacea*) have been traditionally chewed by the Mazatec Indians who call it "the divine food." In 1960, the same Dr. Hofmann who had synthesized LSD and psilocybin, found that ololiuqui contains d-lysergic acid amide and d-isolysergic acid amide, only one-twentieth as potent as LSD, but the first of the naturally occurring lysergic acid derivatives which are hallucinogenic. After Hofmann reported his findings that two common species of morning glory seeds were hallucinogenic, it became clear to a number of psychopharmacologists that a household vine, usually employed to cover unsightly objects or screen out a neighbor's view, had mind-shaking properties. Gradually, the information trickled out to nonprofessionals, and surprising numbers of venturesome individuals without previous interest in gardening began making purchases of such euphonious-sounding morning glory varieties as "Heavenly Blue" and "Pearly Gates." The results of chewing and swallowing the black seeds varied from no reaction whatsoever to "a tremendous experience." [1] Just why a considerable variation in activity occurred, even when similar number of seeds were chewed, is not yet understood. Factors such as the ripeness of the seeds, seasonal alterations in the six active ingredients, even their contamination by fungi, may be related to the inconstant effect. Because of the current interest among North American non-Indians in do-

it-yourself ololiuqui experiences, two insufficiently pub-
licized warnings are offered. Of the six known lysergic
acid derivatives in the morning glory seed, five have
been completely identified. It is possible that some of
the ingredients are capable of constricting small arteries.
If the seeds are taken frequently in large amounts, there
may arise symptoms of ergotism, a circulatory disturbance manifested first by numbness and tingling of the
extremities and culminating in tissue damage to the
fingers and toes. A second caution is that some of the
purchased seeds may be coated with an insecticide which
can be toxic and is, in part, responsible for some of the
nausea, vomiting and diarrhea reported by the morning
glory aficionados.

The price of searching for the other side of reality can
be too high for an occasional unfortunate. The Aztecs
had a name for the winding vine which may be appropriate: "Green Serpent." One young man after sedu-
lously chewing 300 of the black seeds had an intense and
glorious experience for eight hours. The next sixteen
hours were spent in considerable doubt about his ability
to "get back," but he did. Three weeks later the morning
glory state unexpectedly recurred. He was upset and
panicky about the possibility of going crazy. The odd
feelings of strangeness, "looseness" and unreality came
and went for a week. One morning he awoke, agitated
about being "out of balance" again. He dressed, drove
his car down a nearby hill at a speed estimated at 100
miles an hour and crashed into a house.

The ability to purchase dreams in a feed-and-seed
store presents an imposing problem to the authorities,

which may come to be even greater than the difficulties of eradicating the clandestine practice of marihuana smoking. Morning glories grow like weeds; grain farmers look on them as pests, and their elimination is no simple matter. They are also an established part of the American scene. It will be interesting to observe the medico-legal developments of the morning-glory story.

The third of the Mexican triad of potent psychedelics is the peyote cactus (*lophophora Williamsii*) which grows in the watershed of the Rio Grande. An ancient Mexican Indian legend of its origin is about an old man, the forlorn survivor of his tribe who, after a terrible battle, lies down in despair to die. He hears a voice, the voice of peyote, and feels the small cactus in his hand. The voice tells him to get up and find the remnants of his people who have been scattered. He is instructed in the use of peyote and told that it will bring his people courage and peace. The final admonition is: "There are several different ways that you can use me. Unless you use me in only one way, the right way, I may harm you. Use me the right way and I will help you."

The peyote cactus is revered by Indians of the Native American Church. Peyotism is their religion of communion, the core ceremony being an all-night session that begins with the chewing of the sacred peyote. Long periods of silence alternate with peyote songs. Communal feelings of unity and brotherhood are intensely felt. The anthropologist Slotkin asserted that peyotism tends to drive out alcoholism in the tribes that have adopted the practice. Hensley wrote, in a letter to the Commissioner of Indian Affairs, "It cures us of our temporal ills as well as those of a spiritual nature. It takes away the desire for strong drink. I, myself, have been cured of this loathsome disease too horrible to mention. So have hundreds of others. Hundreds of confirmed drunkards have been dragged from their downward way." [2]

Of the twenty-seven peyote derivatives, mescaline is the most important. In the past, peyote and its mescaline have been the major chemical intermediaries between a number of philosophers, authors and artists and their fantasies. Some prominent physicians and writers, from Weir Mitchell and Havelock Ellis to Aldous Huxley, have partaken of either the crude plant or the pure alkaloid.

Long before the arrival of Columbus, from the foothills of the Andes to the Caribbean, cohoba snuff (*Piptadenia peregrina*) was inhaled to promote communal friendliness, convulsive dance rhythms, or a state of intense religious conviction. In larger doses witch doctors used the snuff to induce trances during which the gods and the spirits of the dead were contacted. It is of scientific interest because it contains the chemical bufotenine, which is also a constituent of the amanita mushroom and the skin of certain poisonous toads (from which its name is derived). Bufotenine is inactivated when swallowed, but its activity is retained when it is snuffed or instilled as an enema. The Indians employ both techniques.

Throughout the region drained by the many tributaries of the Amazon, natives prepare a drink from the stems of the *Banisteria caapi* vine. It is a potion of many

names—yagé, ayahuasca or caapi. The single principal
alkaloid has also been variously designated as harmine,
telepathine, yageine or banisterine. The intriguing
name telepathine was coined because the natives employed caapi to find out where lost cows had strayed and
to foretell the future. A century ago the traveler Vil-
lavicencio wrote: "The vine is used to foresee the
question of war or peace, to decipher plans of the enemy,
to take proper steps for attack or defense." In other
words, the Indians believed that a gift of military prophecy was theirs when they were under the influence of
ayahuasca.

But caapi has many other properties. It was also
employed "to welcome foreigners, or, at least, to make
sure of the love of their womenfolk" because it happens
to be one of the few hallucinogens for which an aphro-
disiac property is claimed; clitoral distention and penile
engorgement have been described. Caapi is also an
important part of the Yurupari whipping ceremony.
This is an ordeal of young males of the Colombian
Indian tribes. The potions are imbided by two youths
at a time. While they experience vomiting, blue visions,
and motor excitement, they lash each other with whips
until they drop exhausted and fall into a deep sleep.

Another hallucinogen has been brought back from
the Congo, where the Bantu give it to their young men
to chew. This is the bean or root of *Tabernante iboga*,
and its active ingredient is ibogaine. It is administered
during the initiation rites of the secret societies and
represents both an ordeal and an ecstasy. From personal
experience we can only confirm the physiologic-ordeal

aspect of the drug, not the ecstasy.

It is impressive to contemplate the large array of plant products that despite their poisonous properties have been discovered by simple natives to produce transcendent states. Even those that are not potentially lethal are very unpleasant to take in their natural state. Peyote, for example, is bitter, nauseating and rather emetic for some. That men have succumbed while searching out or experimenting with these mysterious botanicals is not difficult to believe. It can only be concluded that this "other state" fills a need which drove primitive man into a dangerous search for these aids to temporary transformation and self-transcendence. Many of the drugs mentioned have come to be closely associated with religious rites and initiation ceremonies; they have become an integral part of faith in primitive religions. "Taste and see" says the Psalmist, and this is what the native literally does. God and brotherhood become living, palpable realities.

To speak of a religious drug may sound sacrilegious, but it need not be. Many religious movements in an early, fervent stage of their development employed theobotanicals (plants used during religious ceremonies). From the wine of the Christian agape and the Biblical shewbread which contained deliriant herbs and lent the gift of prophecy to the priest who ate it, to the use of tea by Wesley to reinforce an atmosphere of fervent religious fellowship, the assistance of chemical agents was frequently employed.

Drugs are not necessary to induce profound states of

altered awareness. The more traditional efforts have been varied but only sporadically successful. Breathing exercises change the chemical composition of the blood and provide a focus for rhythmic fixation of attention. Many other techniques employ rhythmicity, the hypnotic induction of a trance state, the use of chants, oscillating body movements in prayer, and the whirling of the Maulawiyah dervishes. Fasting, self-flagellation and other forms of mortification have been practiced, not only to assuage guilt or prove devotion, but also to enhance mental awareness.

Body damage can cause a variety of secondary chemical changes; the circulation of toxic products, blood loss, oxygen deficits and other deviations from the state of health induce either a delirium or an attenuation of one's ability to sense reality. Deprivation of any essential process—sleep, for example—can lead to dissociation and loss of contact with reality. Sleep deprivation was practiced by zealots who yearned to lose themselves in themselves. A method much employed both voluntarily and involuntarily has been isolation; the absence of the usual diversity of sensations along with the loss of human contacts is one condition that will remove the common stimuli and concerns. If the flood of sensory data that sweeps in during the waking state can be stilled, the mind seems to lose its ability to orient realistically. These circumstances can disorganize some individuals and produce psychotic symptoms; in others, levels of organization are attained which are called mystical or transcendent. A common thread runs through many of these techniques—they either eliminate the sensory input or make it monotonous or meaningless. The human organism requires a certain minimum of meaningful sensory information, otherwise its survival-oriented thinking slips into fantasy and dreamlike reverie. Though these conditions have at times been called psychotic, some of man's great religions and revelations have had their genesis during such moments.

The LSD story is somewhat different. For centuries, from Spain to Russia, the parasitic fungus ergot spoiled many a rye field during a particularly wet summer. When, through avariciousness, hunger or ignorance, the contaminated flour was baked into bread and eaten, gangrene of the extremities resulted. "St. Anthony's fire" it was called, and the blackened fingers and toes did look charred. Abortions, visual disturbances and mental changes culminating in epidemics of madness after eating spoiled rye flour are also recorded during the Middle Ages. Ergot, the purple fungus, *claviceps purpurea,* is a veritable chemical factory. It contains a large number of active substances, including ergotine, which is used after childbirth to contract the uterus, and ergotamine, used for the treatment of migraine headaches. Lysergic acid is also one of the related constituents, but lysergic acid itself is not hallucinogenic. The mental aberrations of ergotism (the name given to the symptoms resulting from ergot consumption) were probably due to overdoses of the vasoconstricting ergot alkaloids combined with the fearfulness and hysteria engendered by this widespread mutilating affliction.

Not until 1938, when Hofmann added a diethylamide

group to the lysergic acid, did it acquire potent mind-transforming properties; but it was not until 1943, on a warm spring afternoon in the Sandoz Laboratories in Basle overlooking the Rhine, that this psychic effect was discovered. There, in a corner of Switzerland close to the French and German borders, Dr. Hofmann accidentally inhaled or swallowed a minute amount. The following notes were abstracted from Hofmann's notebook by the psychiatrist, W. Stoll.[3]

Last Friday, the 16th of April, I had to leave my work in the laboratory and go home because I felt strangely restless and dizzy. Once there, I lay down and sank into a not unpleasant delirium which was marked by an extreme degree of fantasy. In a sort of trance with closed eyes (I found the daylight unpleasantly glaring) fantastic visions of extraordinary vividness accompanied by a kaleidoscopic play of intense coloration continuously swirled around me. After two hours this condition subsided.

Hofmann suspected a toxic cause and thought in terms of some poisonous solution he might have used. His report continues:

On that Friday, however, the only unusual substances with which I had been in contact was d-lysergic acid and isolysergic acid diethylamide. I had been trying various methods of purifying these isomers by condensation, and also breaking them down into their components. In a preliminary experiment I had succeeded in producing a few milligrams of lysergic acid diethylamide (LSD) as an easily soluble crystal in the form of a neutral tartrate. It was inconceivable to me, however, that I could have absorbed enough of this material to produce the above described state. Furthermore, the symptoms themselves did not appear to be related to those of the Ergotamine-Ergonovine group. I was determined to probe the situation and I decided to experiment upon myself with the crystalline lysergic acid diethylamide. If this material were really the cause, it must be active in minute amounts, and I decided to begin with an extremely small quantity which would still produce some action in equivalent amounts of Ergotamine or Ergonovine.

Hofmann therefore took 250 micrograms of lysergic acid diethylamide, a larger than average amount. After forty minutes he noted "mild dizziness, restlessness, inability to concentrate, visual disturbance and uncontrollable laughter."

At this point the entries in the laboratory notebook end. The last words were written only with the greatest difficulty. I asked my laboratory assistant to escort me home since I assumed that the situation would progress in a manner similar to last Friday. But on the way home (a four-mile trip by bicycle, no other vehicle being available because of the war), the symptoms developed with a much greater intensity than the first time. I had the greatest difficulty speaking coherently and my field of vision fluctuated and was distorted like the re-

flections in an amusement park mirror. I also had
had the impression that I was hardly moving, yet
later my assistant told me that I was pedaling at a
fast pace.

Hofmann's condition intensified until he could barely
communicate.

So far as I can recollect, the height of the crisis
had passed by the time the doctor arrived; it was
characterized by these symptoms: dizziness, visual
distortions, the faces of those present appeared like
grotesque colored masks, strong agitation alternating with paresis, the head, body and extremities
sometimes cold and numb; a metallic taste on the
tongue; throat dry and shriveled; a feeling of suffo-
cation; confusion alternating with a clear appreci-
tion of the situation; at times standing outside myself as a neutral observer and hearing myself
muttering jargon or screaming half madly.

The doctor found a somewhat weak pulse, but in
general a normal circulation. Six hours after taking
the drug, my condition had improved definitely.

The perceptual distortions were still present.
Everything seemed to undulate and their proportions were distorted like the reflections on a choppy
water surface. Everything was changing with unpleasant, predominantly poisonous green and blue
color tones. With closed eyes multihued, metamor-
phizing fantastic images overwhelmed me. Especially noteworthy was the fact that sounds were
transposed into visual sensations so that from each

tone or noise a comparable colored picture was evoked, changing in form and color kaleidoscopically.

After a good night's rest, Hofmann felt "completely well, but tired."

The accidental ingestion of LSD by a perceptive chemist initiated a chain of investigation of the chemically induced mental alterations that has extended into every psychiatric research center. The importance of Hofmann's discovery is not that LSD has any direct chemical relationship to such a disease as schizophrenia; its structure can hardly be expected to be synthesized by the human metabolism. The discovery of LSD has other significant implications: it demonstrates that chemical substances in extremely minute amounts can induce mental distortions that resemble the naturally occurring psychoses; it has stimulated interest in the chemistry of the nervous system, especially the chemical transmitters across the synapse, the nerve-cell connections; and it permits the laboratory study of both normal and abnormal mental processes—an approach to the understanding of such phenomena as attention, imagination and perception as well as hallucinations, delusions and depersonalization becomes possible.

In the few years since Hofmann's serendipity gave us a precise chemical instrument to influence brain metabolism, more than two thousand articles have been written about every aspect of LSD, extending from studies in spider web-building activity to the religious implications of this drug state. The search is far from over. An impressive number of lysergic-acid derivatives with hallucinogenic activity have been synthesized, none quite as potent as LSD itself. Completely new and unrelated chemical groups have also been found to possess similar psychic properties. It seems inevitable that more compounds will appear. More and more pieces are being fitted into the neurochemical jigsaw puzzle. One day the picture will be complete.

The panorama unfolds. The root grubbing, the hit-or-miss leaf chewing of yesterday, gives way to the manufacture of predictably specific synthetic psycho-chemicals. Consciousness changing by design, not by accident, is technologically feasible. It all seems to be a part of man's drive to know what his mind is like and what he is like. Including a search for release from the painful realities of disease, disaster and death, the investigation also attempts to find an answer to the question of how one human should relate to another, and how man should understand his own impermanence.

The current preoccupation with these latter-day mind modifiers ranges from a hedonistic sensuality to a search for the highest of philosophic abstractions, from a tool for deriving scientific data to a sacrament taken to achieve loss of self and union with the ALL.

3 The Research

The known is invariably less provocative than the unknown. However, what is known about LSD and other hallucinogens is almost as fascinating as what remains unknown. Even to a person who has a background of little chemistry and less biology, some of the biochemical data are worthy of attention.

The chemistry of the hallucinogens is to be found in Appendix A. For those interested in reviewing the chemical relationships between the psychotomimetic drugs and the normally occurring chemical conductors of the nervous system this Appendix will be helpful.

THE PHARMACOLOGY

ANIMAL PHARMACOLOGY

LSD and its related compounds have been tested on every laboratory animal species. In addition, an assortment of creatures not ordinarily employed for research purposes have been exposed to the drugs. The results have been less than sensational. If hope existed that a demonstrable animal psychosis might be induced, the results were generally disappointing. Even enormous amounts produced only a variety of physiological effects, such as dilation of the pupil, pilo-erection (the furred equivalent of goose flesh), increased body temperature or a raised blood sugar. These symptoms of stimulation of the sympathetic nervous system can be duplicated by an injection of adrenalin.

It is true that some other responses were also noted. Spiders built a more perfect web under LSD, but a more disarranged one under mescaline, indicating that the spider can distinguish between the two agents better than man. Many species became tamer, and a picture showing Speedy, an aggressive tomcat, under the influence of LSD cowering before an untreated mouse has gained wide distribution in the news media. Abramson has studied the postures of the Siamese fighting fish and the carp. The carp, a species notably resistant to most other drugs, changes from a bottom dweller to a surface swimmer under the influence of LSD.

An elephant was given an enormous dose of LSD (300,000 micrograms) in order to duplicate the recurring musth, a periodic madness of elephants which is accompanied by a secretion from the temporal gland; as a result, the animal convulsed and died.

Undrugged rats placed on a piece of glass inclined sufficiently to start them sliding down, demonstrate characteristic behavior. They seem to become agitated, glance from side to side, press their bodies against the glass, and move their legs in an effort to keep from slipping. Similar behavior can be duplicated with LSD on a level surface.

A series of experiments by Bradley, Cerletti and others have demonstrated that an animal under LSD will respond to a weaker signal (a noise or light) than will an untreated animal. This phenomenon indicates a lowering of the threshold for sensation, and it could be comparable to the enhanced sensory perceptivity in man.

The inability to duplicate the striking subjective phenomena of the LSD state in the animal kingdom should not be too surprising. As Cerletti has stated, if LSD were given to a human who was unable to communicate, it would be extraordinarily difficult to determine what psychological changes were occurring. We have found that some humans make poor subjects to evaluate certain facets of the LSD state.

HUMAN PHARMACOLOGY

One of the astonishing properties of LSD is its intense and lasting action in infinitesimal amounts. It exerts an effect in doses smaller than such potent medicaments as strychnine, cyanide or digitoxin; it is two hundred times more active than cocaine. From one ounce 300,000 adult doses can be obtained. Two pounds, equitably distributed, would mentally dissociate every man, woman and child in Greater New York for an eight-hour period.

An average dose is 100 micrograms (or gamma). This is equivalent to one-tenth of a milligram, or 1/10,000 of a gram, an amount which can barely be seen with the naked eye.

As little as twenty micrograms by mouth can be differentiated from a placebo (a sugar-pill) by most subjects. Some 5 per cent of people will state that no particular changes of any sort occurred after taking 75 to 100 micrograms. One individual has claimed to have taken 3,000 micrograms without complications. The lethal dose for humans is unknown; a death directly due to LSD has not yet been reported in the literature.

When average doses are administered, the onset may be noted within fifteen minutes in sensitive individuals, while in others it may be delayed for an hour or more. Ordinarily the intensity of the symptoms reaches a plateau after one and one-half hours. Although the onset of action after LSD is taken by mouth averages 45 minutes, when given intravenously the effects begin within a few minutes. Only a tenth of the oral dose is required when the spinal route is used, and the action is almost instantaneous. Four hours after consumption the effects start to recede, and they terminate in six to twelve hours. In addition to the oral, intramuscular, intravenous and intraspinal routes, LSD is also effective by inhalation and by absorption from the various mucous surfaces and from abraded skin areas.

The predominance of mental symptoms might lead to the assumption that LSD accumulates in the brain. A number of investigations employing radioactive LSD have found that this is not the case. In fact, the opposite is true. After intravenous injection the brain contains less LSD than other body tissue; the bulk of the radio-active material is found in the small intestine, liver and kidneys. Furthermore, whatever infinitesimal amount does reach the brain is gone within the forty-five-minute period before the drug action commences.

After an average dose has been swallowed, about two hundredths of a microgram (0.00000002 gram) passes through the blood-brain barrier. This would mean that only 3,700,000 molecules of LSD are available for contact with the twelve billion brain cells, and then for only a very few minutes. Such infinite sensitivity of the nerve cells to a transient exposure to LSD can only mean that the drug acts to trigger a chain of metabolic processes which then proceed to exert an effect for many hours afterward.

From the existing evidence it appears that the entire brain is not involved. It is in the diencephalon, or midbrain, that the extraordinary events occur. This region contains the limbic system, which modulates emotional responsivity; the reticular formation, which regulates awareness; and the sympathetic and parasympathetic centers, which control dozens of physiologic functions, from pupil size to body temperature.

This locus of action of LSD is close to the tracts concerned with filtering, comparing and matching sensory information. Here information is enriched with relevant past data, interpreted and evaluated. Decisions about the sense data's importance to the organism induce changes in arousal in some part or all of the brain. The selective adjustments in awareness are very precise and effective. Even in sleep, the doctor wakes to the sound of the telephone, his wife awakens when the baby cries, neither stirs as a street car clatters by, and both may be aroused by a sound of low intensity that is new and unusual. A feedback system from the reticular formation to the inner ear suppresses the registration of unimportant sounds within the sense organ itself. Frequently memories, not sensations, constitute the scanned material. They are recompared, re-evaluated and redeposited on the neuronal protein. Simultaneously, the scanned memories elaborate feeling tones, and they will in turn be elaborated upon by the new feelings. The interplay is so intimate that if the words "thought" or "emotion" were given to this process they would be incorrect—it is an inseparable fusion of the two.

The complex interaction has further ramifications. The ongoing thinking-feeling process modifies and is modified by the body. Discharges down the autonomic nervous system appropriately alter the diameter of the blood vessels, the rhythm of the heart, the cadence of breathing. Every organ, every cell is affected. Reciprocal feedbacks from the tissues to the brain cause readjustments of the level of alertness and the emotion-thought complex. The effects of LSD on this maze of interactivity will be considered later.

To the pharmacologist another intriguing aspect of LSD is the very rapid onset of tolerance. Taken in ordinary amounts daily, after three doses the psychic effects will no longer appear. Three days of abstinence must elapse before tolerance for the drug is lost. A considerable cross-tolerance between mescaline, psilocybin, LSD, and related compounds has been found, indicating that these substances probably impinge upon some common metabolic process. Cross-tolerance between LSD and Ditran (see Appendix A) does not occur, confirming the impression that different chemical systems are involved in these psychochemicals. Abramson's finding that cross-tolerance to LSD can be achieved with large amounts of brom-LSD (a compound devoid of hallucinogenic activity) is provocative. If a chemical cause for schizophrenia is ever uncovered, one logical approach to its treatment will be to manufacture an agent which will produce cross-tolerance to it.

The tranquilizers—chlorpromazine, for example—are excellent antidotes for the hallucinogens. Barbiturates act similarly, by allowing the subject to sleep through the remaining phase of the experience. Such stimulants as amphetamine when combined with LSD elevate the feeling tone and, perhaps, the rate of mental activity.

The common finding of an arousal or alerting brain-wave pattern is not specific for LSD. When electrodes are implanted into the limbic system of animals, paroxysmal electrical activity is recorded. These latter tracings may provide leads concerning the pathways over which the drug acts.

The bodily changes following LSD in man are minor and correspond to those described in animals. The most dependable and constant is enlargement of the pupil. Even bright daylight constricts it only slightly. The pupillary dilation by no means accounts for the intensification of vision; if anything, blurring of perception would be expected with a larger than necessary pupil.

When a physical examination is conducted, a quicker and stronger knee jerk than normal is noted. Blood pressure and pulse rates are unchanged or slightly elevated. A fine tremor might be detected, and the gait is ordinarily unchanged despite the subjective impression that it will be difficult to walk. Speech and other motor acts are either unaffected or only slightly impaired. Loss of appetite is rather constant.

Hallucinogenic substances generally produce few unpleasant physical side effects, and these are often noted early. As Behringer has said, "The hangover precedes the inebriety." [1] LSD is particularly free of uncomfortable symptoms; chilliness and nausea are the only ones mentioned with any frequency. With mescaline, vomiting and dizziness have been reported from time to time. DMT, Sernyl and Ditran (See Appendix A) induce distressing physiologic disturbances much more frequently.

THE PSYCHOLOGY

In an effort to delineate the psychological effects of LSD, hundreds of studies have been done. Normal subjects and all sorts of emotionally ill patients have been tested before, during, and after exposure to the drug. In addition, the contents of their speech, behavior and graphic productions have been analyzed. The effect of varying environmental stresses has been measured. An attempt to condense and order these findings will be made.

Investigations into the psychophysiology of LSD has been a particularly frustrating task. This is due to the enormous difference between subjective sensation and objective measurement. Color is repetitively described in superlatives of intensity, luminescence and saturation. Allan Edwards and I measured color thresholds under LSD. They were unchanged. Despite subjective impressions to the contrary, neither visual nor auditory acuity is improved during the LSD period; in fact, they are decreased.

Change in time perception is one of the notable features that intrigue most subjects. One of them kept remarking on "the eternal present," and another said that the second hand of the clock never moved. The slowdown in time is reminiscent of mental activity during certain moments of personal danger when a large series of memories is recalled within seconds. Mohammed's description of three detailed trips around the earth in the time it took for a water pitcher to fall from his hand to the ground before an epileptic seizure is not unusual in temporal lobe epilepsy. Subjective time normally varies with the metabolic rate, mental activity, the level of alertness and other factors. Clock time is arbitrarily divided into immutable units and does not ordinarily expand or contract. The slowing of subjective time under LSD cannot be demonstrated with a stop watch.

In the same way, the decreased sensitivity to pain which is not uncommonly reported can hardly be demonstrated experimentally. True, the thresholds to warmth and touch are elevated, but not markedly. The relative insensitivity to pain must be considered to be a change in the psychic elaboration of the painful sensation. Very recently Kast compared the degree of pain relief obtained by LSD and by two potent narcotics in fifty terminally ill patients. He found that LSD showed a more effective and protracted analgesic action than Demerol or Dilaudid. In addition to the relief of pain, the patients displayed a "peculiar disregard for the gravity of their situations and talked freely about their impending death with a bland affect considered inappropriate in our Western civilization." [2] This approach to their diseases was usually noted for longer periods of time than the duration of analgesia. It was a common experience for a patient to remark casually on his deadly disease, and in the next breath to comment on the beauty of some visual impression. We can confirm the changed attitude toward dying which LSD can engender. A number of years ago three patients with inoperable cancers were given LSD because they were having great difficulty accepting their impending death. A single exposure to the drug was successful in quieting the agitation of two of them during their final days of life.

Intellectual functioning as measured by the ability to perform well on intelligence tests is worsened. Every investigator, including myself, found that under LSD, abstract reasoning, recall, and arithmetical ability were impaired. In view of the subjects' frequent comment that thinking processes were accelerated, the reduced IQ scores seemed paradoxical. It should be remembered, however, that motivation to perform and attention to the task are important factors in test performance. Both were markedly reduced in all our subjects. They were preoccupied with their LSD experience and did not appear to be concerned about our tests or the importance of our research. Their span of attention was usually diminished, and they spoke of multitudes of thoughts whizzing through their minds so that the test material had to compete with a private flood of ideas.

We found that ego boundaries tended to dissolve and that the separation between the self and the external world became tenuous and sometimes nonexistent. Contact with reality was impaired and survival-oriented thinking became inefficient. The ego defenses—those psychological barriers established to help cope with life stress and to defend the integrity of the personality—were broached, permitting hitherto repressed material to come forth. Sometimes, before their demolition, psychological defenses became exaggerated—for example, paranoid suspiciousness was prominent and dominated the experience in one subject who had shown only minor paranoid trends under control conditions. In others, efforts to keep the personality intact were set aside to a point that differentiation between interior and exterior experience seemed to cease.

The manner in which subjects dealt with the ego-dissolving effects of the drug was of great interest. As soon as change in body image and self concept began to occur, some subjects found the state nonthreatening and relished the loss of their "miserable old selves." Others fought the loss of control, consciously or unconsciously, and proceeded to develop varying degrees of anxiety or somatic aches and pains. Eventually this unwillingness to surrender ego controls was overcome except in those who found it much too threatening to let go. The intellectual defense was the most difficult of all to surmount. By analyzing and rationalizing the events as they occurred, subjects with strong needs to keep intact succeeded in doing so.

43

From the test material it was evident that changes in ego identity were vast. During the height of drug action a complete loss of self-identity was sometimes recorded. Depersonalization—the disruption of one's concept of self—and derealization—the feeling that the outside world was strange—might occur. These are extreme positions on the continuum of human awareness.

Superego functions, such as conscience and the acquired social and cultural customs and rituals, also suffered. Guilt about expressing hostility or shame in connection with the recall of past events which had previously provoked this effect were diminished. Despite a releasing effect upon one's established ethical system, acting-out behavior, including sexual, never occurred in our subjects. The reduction of pressures of an overstrict superego did not result in a total loss of behavioral controls. Attitude measurements demonstrated a decreased dogmatism and a greater tolerance for opposing viewpoints. For at least a short period following the drug exposure, these attitude changes persisted.

A fair portion of the benefits claimed by patients treated with LSD may result from the abandoning of a burdensome, punitive value system and the adoption of one which is more flexible and less constricting. This would also tend to explain the statement of some subjects that a decrease in anxiety occurred following their LSD ingestion even when no therapeutic intent or activity was involved.

From these and related studies a number of assumptions about the psychological effects of LSD can be made. In sufficient amounts this drug has a disinhibiting or releasing action on learned patterns, particularly those related to reality testing, survival functioning, goal-directed behavior and logical thinking. Instead, a primal thinking-feeling process supervenes, in which dreamlike fantasies become prominent. The thin overlay of reason gives way to reverie, identity is submerged by oceanic feelings of unity, and seeing loses the conventional meanings imposed upon the object seen. Color and pattern exist for themselves. Thoughts, creative, bizarre, or nonlogical, are unleashed to flood awareness. Because much is happening, the internal clock seems to be standing still. The LSD exposure appears to produce a reversion to an earlier level of functioning, with each person making this change according to his own personality constellation. Comparisons might be made with the undifferentiated, egoless state of the infant or of certain primitives who exist without self-awareness, but such comparisons, although interesting, are highly speculative.

4 Seeing with All Three Eyes

To understand the changes in sensation and awareness that LSD can call forth, a discussion of normal perception and consciousness must be included.

It is important to realize that the world as we see it is far from an exact image of the physical world. Perception is highly variable and often quite erroneous. One limiting factor is that we perceive only what we can conceive; knowing is prerequisite to seeing and strongly determines what is seen. We tend to see what can be incorporated into our established frame of reference and try to reject that which does not fit it. An American scientist walking in a forest in County Cork at twilight notices something moving in the underbrush; he sees a furred animal. His companion, an old Irishman, clearly sees a leprechaun. In days gone by the world was filled with elves, fairies, hobgoblins, ghosts, and Olympian and Nordic Gods. They were seen because people believed in them. Nowadays they are very scarce.

Furthermore, it is impossible to see things as they actually are with our optical system. From my window the island called Catalina, visible far out in the Pacific, appears in the light of the setting sun smooth and deep blue. If we were on it, it would look rugged and green. The island sits low on the horizon, a solid and immobile mass. Our physicists tell us that it is really inhabited by clumps of lonely protons and neutrons at the center of planetary systems of whirling masses of electrons. Farther to the west the sun seems to be getting larger and redder as it sinks into the sea. I am aware of the optical illusion, but cannot see it otherwise. Wherever we turn, such illusions confront us. Whether they are in the parallax of the straight lines of railroad tracks, or in the deliberate optical deceptions in a painting or a woman's gown, they surround us. We have learned to live with our misperceptions. If an artist did not impose the artifice of perspective, we would find his work odd and, perhaps, call it primitive. The BaMbuti jungle dwellers who have never seen farther than a few feet, because of the thickness of the overgrown Ituri forest, have developed no sense of perspective. When one was taken out of the wilderness and saw a cow grazing in a valley far below, he was astonished at the existence of a tiny animal so much like the cow in his small jungle clearing.

After our eyes have processed the image, the light-waves are converted to minute electrical currents and transmitted along nerve fibers to the visual cortex of the brain. What has been seen undergoes a further gross deformation here. W. R. Brain described it well: "When we look at a circle drawn on a piece of paper, the image that the cerebral cortex finally perceives is halved, reduplicated, transposed, inverted, distorted and three dimensional." Since this same deforming process happens to all of us, we are able to validate each other's erroneous perceptions.

An investigation done many years ago demonstrates how quickly and completely visual readjustments can be made. A number of subjects were fitted with eyeglasses whose lenses were designed to produce inverted vision. At first they found it very confusing to manage in an upside-down world. Within a few days, however, corrections in the visual field began. First, bodies of water came into their proper places—namely, down instead of up. Eventually, with continued wearing of the glasses, everything was seen as it had been prior to the experiment. When the glasses were removed, the world was immediately topsy-turvy again, and a second relearning period was necessary before things were back to their "normal" positions in space.

Thus the world is seen, not as it is, but as it ought to be. We have acquired a perceptual set which reworks the seen into the known. The sky is up, the sea and earth are down. If they happen to be found in another position, given time the mind will correct the "error."

The perceptual set is part of our mammalian and human endowment. Certain visual absolutes seem to exist with which most will agree. We all assume, for example, that two things cannot occupy the same place at the same time and that the space between objects is empty. The set also varies with the individual and his own values. The lumberman and the artist do not see a tree in the same way. A passerby may look at, but not see the tree at all. Each man's percepts are modified by his assumptive set.

The perceptual apparatus focuses on the new and the unexpected. It orients itself toward the unusual or the moving. The commonplace is neglected, the routine becomes a part of the background and may not register in awareness at all. The first sensory experience is frequently the most lasting and meaningful; repetition eventually dulls its pristine sparkle. The simple wonders of childhood may be remembered but hardly recaptured. It was the first shiny penny, the first spinning top, the first piece of chocolate that was the best of all. Then the extraordinary becomes ordinary, the vivid fades, the brilliant dulls. The guard at the Louvre does not look up as he walks past the Titians, the Goyas and the da Vincis. The jaded traveler reads his newspaper while the magic of New York after dark unfolds below his plane.

Only a very few are able to retain the novelty of the first sensory experience after repeated exposures. One of the unique qualities of LSD is its capacity to temporarily bring back the vividness of newness.

It should not be inferred that the vagaries of perception preclude a satisfactory validation of what is observed. Each cultural group shares an approximately common perceptual set; the errors cancel out. Still, it ought not be assumed that because all of us describe objects in the same way they are therefore really like that.

Our ability to agree upon the nature of the external

world rapidly breaks down when a strong emotional charge is attached to the thing perceived. Two individuals, or two nations, will see an event in diametrically different ways if strong and contrary emotions are involved.

The impact of mood upon perception is greatly increased during the LSD state. Euphoric subjects describe colors as bright and gay; should they become depressed the colors darken or are bleached out. The observer might come to appear sinister, whereas in a lighter mood he was considered friendly.

What has already been said indicates that believing is as much a part of seeing as seeing is believing. Perception is variable and less than perfect. Our notions of what is "out there" seem to be based upon an indistinct uncertainty. For all we know, the thing called reality may exist, but we shall never see it. What we call reality is a shadow upon an imperfect screen. Korzybski used the analogy that a map stands in the same relationship to the territory it covers as our idea of reality stands to reality.

Our visual mechanism must have evolved with the goal of keeping the organism viable rather than with the aim of seeing things as they are. Under the effects of LSD this goal may be reversed. Perception ceases to subserve meaning and becomes a *Ding an Sich*. A red traffic light may be, not a danger signal, but an object of surpassing beauty. No doubt it is both, but recognition of its symbolic meaning keeps us alive.

The enormous intensification of color and the transformation of the object into a perceptual, rather than a rational, composition, are not simply due to "newness" or a fracture of the perceptual set. In the LSD condition an ability to exclude the clutter of random distractions also becomes possible. The complete focus is on the object; extraneous time-space considerations cease to impinge. This total awareness Meister Eckhart calls "the now moment." A few people can experience such total attention spontaneously. With LSD this timeless, selfless relationship with the percept is achievable by many. When it happens, the object is invested with a profound significance. The separation between the one who sees and the seen vanishes. As one subject said, "Everything is coming apart at the seams."

A more common and less esoteric occurrence, the appearance of flowing, colorful geometric patterns that slant past behind closed eyes, is one of the hallmarks of the LSD state. These elusive, mobile tapestries could have their origin within the eyeball. It has been found in both animals and man that under LSD the retinal cells "fire" in the absence of a light stimulus. The swirling colors and wallpaper designs spilling across the private visual screen are quite compatible with LSD-induced electrical discharges from the retina. However, similar discharges also result from stimulating the temporal lobe of the brain.

The apparent movement of fixed objects, the "breathing" of flowers, the undulation of walls, the transformation of faces, and the like must also be accounted for. Even the perception of food may be affected: "I could eat very little of a wriggling, writhing stuffed pepper." These are more complex illusions, and a more complex explanation is probably required. It has been found that when an image falls upon the same retinal cells for over one-fifth of a second, the image will disappear. To maintain constant vision, the eye is in perpetual micro-movement. These invisible quiverings throw the image onto new cells of the retinal mosaic, permitting continuous vision and recovery of the cells that had exhausted their visual purple. If LSD interferes with these minute eye movements, a physiologic basis for the illusion will have been found. But there is more to the phenomenon, for these illusions of movement commonly carry symbolic overtones. A fresh and vibrant blossom may change to a drooping, faded flower under one's gaze. This metamorphosis will correlate well with the existing emotional situation. It is assumed that the illusory movement of surfaces provides a vehicle for the projection of the interior emotional tone onto the perceived object.

The changes in sensory perception other than visual should be noted. Hearing is sometimes intensified, and listening to music may be described as an exceedingly esthetic experience. Modifications of touch sensation are also mentioned; they usually consist of heightened sensitivity to texture and feelings of tingling and numbness of the hands and feet. Changes in taste and smell are infrequently reported; when they occur, they are enhanced.

Subjects often remark upon synesthesias—cross-overs of sensation from one sense modality to another. For example, the subject will say that he can hear colors, or he will speak of the scent of music. Such a stimulus as clapping of the hands may induce changes in the color and texture of the kaleidoscopic patterns seen behind closed eyes. Synesthesias may represent the overflow of sensory excitation onto circuitry from which it is ordinarily suppressed. They occur under normal conditions when the sensation is very strong—the "seeing stars" effect after a blow on the head being one example. Hallucinations will be considered in a later chapter, for they are caused by thinking-feeling disturbances rather than by visual aberrations.

The condition called sensory deprivation is of interest to those who are trying to understand hallucinogenic activity. Sensory deprivation consists of the reduction or elimination of stimuli from the outside. Taste and smell are easy to obliterate; sight is eliminated by providing a complete blackout. The total elimination of sound is technically difficult, but it can be accomplished. Touch and the internal body sensations cannot be eliminated, but a partial reduction can be achieved by the use of thick gloves and foam rubber. A related state is called sensory invariance or sensory monotony. In these conditions the effort is to eliminate meaningful incoming signals by making stimuli continuous and meaningless. Ground-glass goggles are worn, and "white noise," a perpetual staticlike sound, is piped into the ears.

It may be noted that a limited environment as procured by the deprivation or invariance of sensory input is to be found in places outside a research laboratory. Cave explorers come upon it when they sit quietly in the depths of the earth. Solitary shipwrecked sailors or snowbound and isolated Arctic dwellers may experience the state. Even elderly patients with bandaged eyes and restricted movements following the removal of cataracts are prone to deprivation symptoms. The sensory monotony of the radar watch or the truck driver on long desert runs is a source of dangerous misperceptions. Solitary confinement for punitive or brainwashing purposes is an extreme form of deprivation, for in addition to the fearfulness of the situation, it is combined with sleep and nutritional deprivation.

Perhaps the visions of the ascetics were in part the results of social and sensory deprivation. Vitamin deficiencies, malnutrition and physical illness may also have played a role. Without a doubt emotional turmoil and the intensity of their meditative practices were important contributory elements.

When employed scientifically, sensory deprivation takes one of two forms. In the Lilly-Shurley type of experiments the subjects are provided with a breathing helmet and are immersed in a tank of tepid water. In addition to the loss of the usual sensory information, the awareness of one's position in space is also impaired. After only a few hours mental changes develop. In the Hebb type of sensory exclusion the volunteer lies on a bed in a soundproof cubicle, wearing frosted goggles and cotton gloves with inverted cardboard cuffs which extend beyond the fingertips. A liquid diet and toilet facilities are periodically provided. The subject is monitored, but he is not permitted the stimulus of conversation with the monitor. Although an occasional subject is able to tolerate the situation for a week, most of the paid volunteer subjects withdraw from the experiment much earlier.

The effects of prolonged diminution of sense input are remarkable. After a few days, organized thinking is impaired and dreamlike ruminations intervene. The subject may become petulant, mildly suspicious, or even confused about his situation. A mixture of visual pseudohallucinations and hallucinations may ensue; more rarely, auditory and tactile misperceptions are reported over the recording system.

The hallucinatory activity is of interest because it is reminiscent of that induced with psychedelic drugs. Patterned images are often seen and are described as wallpaper or stroboscopic designs. One subject saw a file of prehistoric monsters walking, another experienced a pastoral landscape, a third watched a series of animated cartoons. One subject declared that he had just awakened from a vivid dream but that the dream was still going on. Some heard distant music, people talking or sounds of machinery. The misperceptions did not engender excessive anxiety. In fact, some subjects rather enjoyed them as a relief from boredom. In this connection an occasional prisoner has been known to actually request solitary confinement for the purpose of savoring the dissociated state.

Sleep and waking became difficult to distinguish. Feelings of depersonalization, sensations of strangeness, even splitting of the body image may arise. Some subjects "floated" around the room yet could "look" down and see themselves sprawled on the bed. Tests of motor function, judgment and mental arithmetic were poorly performed, and these deficiencies lasted for hours or days after the experiment was terminated.

It appears that the human brain, unlike the computer, cannot be idle for long periods and still maintain its efficiency. Unless it receives a flow of varying sensory fodder, a dreamlike state emerges. We seem to need information for mental effectiveness as much as we need food for physical health.

Sensation has a dual function. It not only provides specific data on what is seen, heard, felt, etc., but it also regulates the level of arousal of various parts of the brain. It is in the brain stem reticular formation that adjustments in mental excitation occur. When environmental stimuli become monotonous or scanty, reticular formation activity is reduced and alertness diminishes.

Many of the signs of sensory deprivation are similar to those seen from time to time with LSD. Table 1 (see Appendix B) demonstrates that the symptoms reported under both conditions overlap, although the intensity may be greater with the drug.

The implication that conditions analogous to the LSD state can be achieved by excluding sensory input is illuminating. It raises the issue of the neurophysiological mechanism of LSD action. Perhaps it blockades incoming sensation. This can scarcely be true for LSD, but preliminary findings support the blockade theory for hallucinogens of the Ditran and Sernyl categories. Elkes has suggested that LSD may alter the coding of incoming messages, and we have compiled some partial confirmation of this theory. Since sensory deprivation and LSD produce alterations that approximately resemble each other, we assumed that if LSD were given to subjects during a state of sensory impoverishment, the effects would be magnified. To our surprise, half of our subjects (who had never had LSD before), given 125 gamma experienced no effects at all during a two-hour stay in a sensory deprivation cubicle. Only after the cubicle door was opened and light and sound began to register on their eyes and ears did they start to feel the effects of LSD. That sensory deprivation can abort the LSD reaction in some people is suggestive evidence that the coding mechanism is one of the affected sites. If there is nothing to code, no changes will occur.

Equal interest attaches to the 50 per cent of our subjects who had the expected or even intensified effects from combining LSD with two hours of sensory deprivation. It is assumed that people can be subdivided into two types, depending on their reliance on the environment. There is a field dependent group, who uses incoming sensory data predominantly to "keep in touch." Such persons correspond to those who noticed no effects from LSD when their sensory cues were cut off. A second type are the field-independent individuals, who do not require external information as much and rely more on internal information. When such people receive LSD in a limited environment, they proceed to have the expected experience. They might even find that the total elimination of light and sound enhances their reaction.

This work is far from conclusive. Longer periods of deprivation than two hours must be studied; techniques must also be developed to predict who will and who will not have the LSD effect neutralized by cutting off the flow of sensory information. It should be added that each subject was tested four times, twice under sensory deprivation and twice under normal sensory conditions. In each condition he was administered LSD or an identical-appearing placebo. After two hours the subject was asked to guess what he had received. None of the guesses were wrong except when sensory deprivation was combined with LSD. In this condition six of twelve subjects claimed that they had received a placebo when, in fact, the drug had been given. Soon after coming out of the "black box," they changed their minds. We did not depend solely on the statement of the subject. Continuous measurements of heart and respiration rates, skin resistance, finger blood flow and brainwave tracings were made. The results show that when LSD is given under normal conditions, a certain physiologic pattern emerges. When the placebo is administered under conditions of sensory deprivation, a different pattern is seen. With sensory deprivation plus LSD, the resulting physiologic response lies between these two patterns.

A further implication of the relationship between sensory isolation and LSD is that the state may not merit the adjective "toxic" if it also occurs in the absence of a toxin. It seems that we are dealing with a state of mental activity which is the final product of many initiating factors. We suspect that yoga breathing exercises, contemplative meditation (concentration without thinking), and the "break-off" phenomenon during high-altitude flying are related. Probably hypnagogic imagery—those visions that a few people see in the period between sleeping and waking—fit in here. Some of the hypnotic trance effects fall into this peculiar condition. During hypnosis immobilization of posture, gaze and awareness is required. An unvarying or rhythmic stimulus of low intensity is used for induction of the trance. There is suppression of all incoming sensory material except the point of focused concentration. Under hypnosis, as in other conditions where the peripheral distractions are eliminated and the scanning mechanism is coned down, the mind operates on an unaccustomed level. This heterogenous group could be called a "dissociated" state, for a disruption of ordinary conscious-unconscious relationships is the common finding. A comparison with the microscope may be permissible here: if ordinary consciousness is represented by the low-power lens, which surveys a broad area, the dissociated states can be compared to the high-power lens, which examines a tiny area but reveals elements unseen with the lesser magnification.

It is difficult to consider perception without dealing with consciousness, the eye that looks within. It has already been indicated that perception modulates consciousness through the reticular formation of the midbrain. Naturally levels of consciousness in turn modify the percept.

Just what makes an organism aware of its own awareness has puzzled centuries of philosophers and decades of scientists. W. R. Brain, the neurologist, has put the relationship between the brain and consciousness as well as anyone: "Not only are there twelve thousand million nerve cells out of which the patterns can be made, but nervous patterns exist in time, like a melody, as well as in space. If you look at a tapestry through a magnifying glass you will see the individual threads but not the pattern; if you stand away from it you will see the pattern but not the threads. My guess is that in the nervous system we are looking at the threads, while in the mind we perceive the patterns, and that one day we shall discover how the patterns are made of the threads." [1] Just as one thread cannot make a tapestry, a single nerve cell cannot produce a thought. Even the simplest mental activity requires assemblies of neurons acting as a synchronized functioning unit. Thoughts are, in effect, patterns of neuronal discharges.

Our ordinary span of consciousness varies from deep sleep to deep concentration. Innumerable gradations between the two extremes exist. Waking awareness is not a fixed, immutable constant, but varies according to the ambient temperature, fatigue, interest in the task and a dozen other variables. Intense concentration is a satisfactory but not a total convergence of attention. Beyond deep concentration, further increments are possible to a maximal state which can hardly be named scientifically at this time. Just as perception can be pinpointed and all extraneous distractions eliminated under LSD and allied conditions, so the scanning beam of awareness can be focused on a minute area to the exclusion of all peripheral thought. These brief "superconscious" bursts have not been satisfactorily studied with precision methods, and their analyses will be most difficult. In the religious and philosophic literature, such names as religious experience, cosmic consciousness, and integral thought have been applied to analogous states. No neuroanatomic reason exists to suggest that we are not capable of rare and transient transactions of superlative knowing.

It is hardly necessary to invoke supernatural explanations for the mind's more exceptional activities. What is necessary is to begin to appreciate the potential of this instrument. Its organization and complexity is difficult to grasp. The brain receives millions of electrical impulses every second. The twelve billion brain cells each have up to 25,000 interconnections. Each cell is capable of storing numerous bits of information. These items need not pass through conscious awareness before being laid down as memory. The retrieval system and the mechanisms for matching the present with the past are phenomenal; and in the conditions we have been describing, they may reach an unbelievable peak of performance. Intuition, creativity, telepathic experiences, prophecy—all can be understood as superior activities of brain-mind function.

It is here, in the higher levels of organization of this immense network of networks, that Gerald Heard's "growing edge" of man's development will be found. The mind's surmised and still unknown potential is our future. The experience called hallucinogenic will play a role in leading us into the future. It points out the existence of unique mental states which must be carefully studied and understood.

Currently we use a continuum of mental functioning which places sanity at one end and insanity at the other. Those prophets, mystics and gods to whom we do not subscribe are called mad. Those we believe in are considered divinely inspired. That some were mad is certain. But others encountered surpassing states of awareness and returned with the conviction that they had attained the truth. They then proceeded to change their way of life and ours. On the basis of these hyperconscious moments, most of the great religions of the world have been founded.

Handsome Lake, for example, a Seneca of the Iroquois confederation, saw his people deteriorate within a generation from a powerful, proud nation into a pathetic, hungry, homeless remnant. His own situation mirrored the ruin of his tribe. In the spring of 1799 he was a hopeless bedridden drunkard, brooding over his sinfulness and the loss of his family. During that year he had a series of visions that transformed his life and that of the Senecas. Having given up drink and recovered his health, he preached a doctrine of sobriety, industry and dependability. The effects were remarkable. The Senecas transformed themselves from a frontier slum society into a vigorous and enterprising community. Even today some aspects of the Handsome Lake religion survive on the Iroquois reservations of New York and Ontario.

The relationship of such religious experiences to the psychotic process is a difficult and delicate problem. Are the visions of a prophet revelation or disease? Does schizophrenia encompass both the delusional paranoiacs and the holy men whose trances have provided us with messages which many consider gospel? The psychedelic drugs have a contribution to make in the understanding of such matters. Under their influence episodes of psychotic disorganization are certainly possible. In other instances they have induced an experience of psychic integration which has been called identical with the spontaneous religious experience by people who have known both states. Mental disorganization results in a psychosis; a creative reorganization underlies the visionary state. Should this state, entered into with or without chemical aid, also be called insanity? It would seem more appropriate to differentiate it and call it *unsanity* in view of the constructive solutions that can arise from it. Then, unsanity would properly be placed at one end of the continuum and be polar to insanity. Somewhere in the middle zone lies sanity. But the continuum is no straight line. It is bent into a circular shape with a narrow gap, where the poles of insanity and unsanity are almost joined. "Great wits to madness nearly are allied" said Dryden. Nearly, but not quite. In this great wheel of awareness, sanity resides in what we call the conscious. Both insanity and unsanity lie in the unconscious.

A geography of unsanity has not yet been mapped. But it would include the "Peak Experience" of Maslow, who has collected thousands of great moments of rapture, bliss and ecstasy from the lives of ordinary people who were overcome by flashes of beauty, love, sexual experience, perfection, awe, esthetic or creative wonder or insight. Visionary experience as described by such writers as William Blake or Æ is of this order. The *satori* of Zen Buddhism, the Hindu *moksha,* and *samahdi* of Vedanta belong here, along with the recorded mystical, prophetic and religious experiences of East and West.

In such a model, sanity is far from downgraded. It is the best state of mind for surviving, for the selling and the buying that life requires. Vehicles should only be driven by the sane, during insane and unsane intervals the necessary motivations and psychomotor skills being insufficient. We need more, not less, sanity. Unfortunately common sense and realistic thinking are not as free from illogic and unreason as might be hoped. Science and technology require the best sanity we possess. Only a dash of unsanity is needed from time to time. For religion and the arts, the experience of unsanity is important. Most artists know this. Verlaine, Van Gogh, Coleridge and Baudelaire among others have left tragic accounts of their efforts to break through the barriers of reason and reality.

5 The Mind Nobody Knows

The mind—that seven inches of inner space between the root of the nose and the occiput—is our prized possession. Its study on every level is most important. Our future evolution lies as much in our minds as in our genes. A major portion of our heredity will occur outside the cell, even outside the organism. We shall evolve principally by the external inheritance of the products of the mind—the arts and the sciences. Cultural, technological and scientific information stored in people, in books, those original teaching machines, and in computers will be the destiny of man.

We must learn as much as possible about this vehicle of our evolution; the full responsibility for its direction is ours. Knowledge about the substructure of the emotions is particularly vital. Unless the race breaks out of its legacy of predatory destructiveness, the lethal weaponry which our intellects have created will annihilate us. Murderous aggression is no innate, immutable drive, but it is an innate potential that need never become manifest with enlightened education of the mind and particularly of the emotions.

Nor need we fear the bogy of control of the mind. Mind control has been with us from the time a Cro-Magnon man showed his son how to fashion a spear point. Since then our minds have been controlled by parents, teachers, pastors, politicians and every other successful communicator. What must be avoided is mind control by the ignorant, the sick and the power seeker.

The psychochemicals of today, and those to come, are suspect by those who fear that they will be robotized by these drugs' insidious influence. They visualize a sort of dictatorship without tears. This is certainly a possibility. Just as atomic energy, automobiles and food can be misused, so can agents which exert a potent influence on the mind be exploited. But like atomic energy, automobiles and food, they also offer the promise of notable benefits.

To completely understand the mind, it is not enough to examine the overlay of sanity and the recesses of insanity. The vortex of unsanity must be studiously approached and somehow tapped. The hallucinogens are one approach to this zone of danger and of hope.

The nature of the thinking process under LSD is most difficult to describe. It must be kept in mind that the spectrum of thinking varies from an amorphous, dreamy bemusement to clear, integrated mental activity and from blatant delusions to mile-a-minute mental activity.

Under LSD, a single thought may branch out into a vast hierarchy of related subthoughts, all connected but much too complex and elusive to describe. Each ramification becomes a shifting, coalescing, elaborating network. To do more than contemplate the composition is futile. Its translation into words captures only broken fragments. The listener might label the content a manic flight of ideas. Actually the mental productions may be orderly until speech is attempted. Just as Heisenberg's measurements changed the path of the subatomic particles he was measuring, so attempts to transmit what is happening in the LSD state changes the happening.

These highly complicated ideational structures are probably caused by a flood of associations which are ordinarily suppressed. It is as though the nerve net has been reset at a lower threshold, permitting the transmission of masses of associations normally denied passage. If this is the mechanism, the releasing effect must occur at the synapses. These synapses—which Gerard calls "the decision points of the nervous system"—say "no" much less frequently after contact with LSD. The reduction of synaptic inhibition is also a possible explanation of the penetration of emotional and visual components into thought processes.

In addition to transformations in the quantity of thinking, the quality of thinking undergoes modifications. It becomes eidetic—that is, the idea becomes visible. The capability to see thoughts is a commonplace experience for about 10 per cent of the population under normal conditions. Under LSD thought is fascinatingly, even distractingly vivid. A recalled memory has an unexpected dimensionality, detail and veraciousness.

Ideas also acquire a strong emotional component. Overtones of powerful feelings are joined to thought. One recognizes that the separation of thinking from feeling must have been a recent evolutionary development. In the LSD state they are hardly separable. It is not that one modifies the other, one *is* the other.

In the prelogical world of LSD, thought and emotion are inseparable. Thinking is joined to the weather of the mood and the climate of the affect, becoming idiosyncratic and novel, and is expressed with much less critical surveillance. Such adjectives as bizarre, imaginative, schizophrenic or creative have been applied to the phenomenon, depending upon the judgment of the end product and the persuasion of the judge. The expression "knight's move thinking" clearly characterizes the tendency to skip around and over premises and syllogisms. The "as if" capacity of the mind is impaired. A thing that is like the other becomes the other in the predicate logic of analogy.

Mental function can become concrete to the point where a proverb is not understood in its abstract meaning. "A rolling stone gathers no moss" may be interpreted as "If a stone is rolling downhill, moss has no time to grow on it." On the other hand, such philosophic generalities as "Why should man pretend when he is?" "We must think in many categories" or "There is no ugliness" come forth effortlessly. One is reminded of Sir Humphry Davy's century-old encounter with nitrous oxide and his scribbling, "The universe has no opposite" as his contribution to the Ultimate Truth. In this mental state Zen-like inconsistencies become consistent, ambiguous or incompatible concepts are tolerated and paradoxes cease to be paradoxes.

Memory is oddly affected by LSD. On the one hand the sort of memory required for tasks like repeating a series of numbers backward is impaired. On the other hand the recall of remote events may be exceedingly accurate in minutest detail. Recall is particularly affected by the brain's normal inhibitory activity. Often we must "think aside" in order to remember a name, or we must sleep on an unremembered fact in order to bring it back: analytic thinking interferes with the associations required for some kinds of remembering. "Alert passivity" is the state that Roger Fry describes as the best for recall, the appreciation of a work of art or the achievement of total attention. Alert passivity is a fair description of certain LSD states.

Delusional thinking has been observed, and altogether paranoid ideas have been expressed without any insight that they are incorrect. One subject had the delusion that "All this is a plot, everything that is happening has been planned and staged to produce an effect on me." More frequently the false idea is entertained but only given partial credence—in effect, a sort of "demidelusion." It is the cognitive equivalent to the pseudo-hallucination which is also not quite believed. It might be expressed as "The people in the restaurant looked like actors who were playing a role. Everything seemed contrived, but I knew that it was too much trouble to go to, just to influence me, so I figured it was my imagination."

An examination of hallucinations requires some definite frame of reference through which to view the phenomenon. This frame of reference is not yet firmly established. In past centuries hallucinations were thought to be real visitations from the spirit world. Depending on the interpretation of the community, their celestial or satanic origin was determined. The French loyalists believed that Joan of Arc's visions were from God; the English judged them to be inspired by the devil. Today certain subcultures still give credence to the spiritual nature of visionary phenomena. Often the hallucinator gains considerable status within his group. The Eskimos elect as their religious leader the person fortunate enough to hallucinate. Ruth Benedict describes the extent to which the Plains Indian went to procure an hallucination:

> On the western plains men sought these visions with hideous tortures. They cut strips from the skin of their arms, they struck off fingers, they swung themselves from tall poles by straps inserted under the muscles of their shoulders. They went without food or water for extreme periods. They sought in every way to achieve an order of experience set apart from daily living.[1]

Even in our sophisticated society the dream and the hallucination retain a vestige of their magical powers. Many surmise that somehow they contain a more im-

portant message, a final truth of which waking awareness
is incapable. Dreams and hallucinations contain information to be decoded, but whether their truth has a
"higher" or "deeper" quality is uncertain. Current
medical judgment about a full-blown hallucination is
that, unless it is caused by a toxin or by physical illness,
it is symptomatic of a serious mental disturbance.

Smythies assumes that hallucinations are part of the
normal child's psychic experience. As the individual
grows older, they diminish and are eventually suppressed
because of their current negative social value. From
what is known of the mental activity underlying our
rational mind, his assumption may be correct. Freud
said that a psychosis was a waking dream. Similarly, a
dream represents the psychosislike fantasies of the sleeping, disinhibited mind.

What position should be taken regarding the nature
of the complex, detailed, well-formed, "realer than real"
hallucinations seen under LSD? Some subjects have
asserted that "They could hardly have come from me. I
do not know nor have I ever experienced these things."
They assumed that the hallucinations had their genesis
elsewhere, possibly in the Jungian collective unconscious
or even in past lives. It seems more likely that the visions
seen under the drug are projections of internalized
conflicts, emotional discharges, a visual overflow from
the deep pool of "primary-process" thinking. The primary process, the mental activity of the unconscious
mind, is the stuff of which dreams, hypnagogic imagery,
sensory deprivation and the LSD states are made. It is
the fount of the psychotic's productions and the well-

spring of artistic, sometimes scientific, creation.

Often the symbolism of the productions is obviously compatible with Freudian psychodynamics. At other times its interpretation is more obscure. In a picturesque metaphor Aldous Huxley describes the levels of cerebral activity as an Old World of one's consciousness, while beyond the sea lies a series of New Worlds—the not too distant Virginias and Carolinas of the personal unconscious, the Far West of the collective unconscious and across another, vaster ocean, at the antipodes of everyday consciousness, the mental world of Australia, where creatures at least as strange as the platypus and the wallaby roam. Although the antipodes of the mind are recondite and the fauna improbable, they do seem to conform to the peculiar paralogic of the unconscious. The strange terrain and the implausible creatures are myths and metaphors of our own creation, although we cannot ordinarily recognize them.

The pictorial aspects of the LSD experience can dominate, can even inundate the subject in an immense surge of chromatic imagery. Part of a tape recording from an insurance counselor follows, an example of rich hallucinatory fabrications. He saw a personal Fantasia, courtesy of lysergic acid diethylamide:

Now, the movies are really starting. Some wonderful multicolored geometric patterns; brilliant fireworks, too. And they are coming and changing a thousand frames a second. But there is something funny about them; they are all taking place twenty thousand leagues under the sea.

There is something tremendously oscillating about these underwater scenes—from pleasant to unpleasant, then pleasant again, then once more unpleasant, in rapid rotation. On the pleasant side: some really beautifully illuminated fish, not like any real fish I ever saw before—more fish designs than fish—but moving by the millions, as if they were real illuminated fish. On the unpleasant side, when my beautiful fish flow away, there are some gigantic underwater spider webs, composed of luminous threads, pretty to look at, but threatening at the same time—as are the huge and delicately colored sea anemones lurking nearby. All this has a sort of Dali-like dimension to it; but too much of this is now dominated by the spider webs and foreboding sea anemones. . . .

I really ought to call this the Purple Stage. For right now I'm seeing everything in a purple aura, a pleasant and pretty violet purple. If the images were coming fast before, they are coming ten times faster now. Mountains upon mountains, hundreds of them—stretching out into eternity—all colored with this lovely purple hue . . . mountains of the moon. Only, just mountains; no people; just mountain upon mountain.

Now the romantic mood is really going strong— mountains of the moon shift back to earth, but still retain a strong Tibetan Shangri-La flavor. And now India and Hinduism comes into these fantasies, and in a strange manner: mountains melt into elephants; and elephants grow and grow into mountains again; mountains dissolve into all sorts of strange animal shapes;

then each animal expands out and becomes an entire celestial sphere. It is as if the mountains, as Mother Earth, breathed and took animal forms; and then these forms dissolved and, expanding, became new planets, each a replica of Mother Earth. . . .

Now these reveries are getting as erratic as some of those futuristic motion pictures they experimented with some years ago. I'm inside a church now. It has lovely stained-glass windows. The designs are geometric and beautiful. But it is all changing to undersea forms again. And this time I'm really an underseas captive. I'm being pinned to the bottom of the ocean floor by thongs of undersea weeds, cleverly spun around my arms and legs by hundreds of Lilliputians. But these are the silliest Lilliputians you ever saw—actually, they are the seven dwarfs from Snow White, multiplied a couple of hundred times over, and they sure are off base, as they shouldn't be in this underseas scene at all. But here they are; and while they are tying me down pretty tightly, it all has the flavor of a playful game.

My little Lilliputian playfellows are gone. Sex has come to replace them. But this isn't sex in any bedlike manner. This sex world is all Freud. And it is all about a tunnel. And it is not entirely a new tunnel; quite clearly I can identify it as a tremendous unfolding on a tremendously magnified scale, of a much smaller, never as fully visualized, and promptly suppressed tunnel, that, some fifteen years ago, I dimly saw, off and on, during some two years of unproductive psychoanalysis. Then I reported such a tunnel, off and on, to the analyst; but at that time it never broke fully into consciousness; its insides were never clearly seen; nor did anything discernible and reportable ever come out of it.

Actually, this is not a tunnel but a vast cave, if you can call a cave, something that is miles long. Think of a straight-line natural cavern, and you have it. Only this cavern is a vast, primordial vagina. It is not the vagina of any female who ever lived. It is just vagina incarnate. In dimensions, it is a cavern; but a cavern the walls of which are a pulsating, throbbing, vaginal material—decorated, if you will, with hundreds of breasts. Out of this vaginal cavern, a sticky, beige-color plasticine sort of material is endlessly flowing. Marvels of creativity occur, as this material emerges. It is an entirely uncontrolled self-creativity: perfect art, without any artist.

This consummate art is achieved by the plasticine material itself as, gushing out of the cavernous vagina, it thins out in viscosity, takes on a new delicate ivory hue and molds itself endlessly like a thousand and one pieces of statuary. At the beginning this statuary once again has a distinctly Hindu aura: the whole pantheon of Hindu deities, gods and goddesses flow gently past in unending procession. Then the creed changes and the exquisite ivory forms become a panoply of Buddhas and Bodhisativas. Now India leaves the scene and is replaced by statuary of rich Persian design, as if figures had walked off Persian vases and pottery and enlarged a hundredfold, were remolded and recast in the now ivory-colored plasticine substance still endlessly flowing from the mammoth vaginal cavern. Persia recedes, and now I recognize the creations as vast copies of the figures in Michelangelo's paintings in the Sistine Chapel. I do not feel that I am either painter or sculptor; yet, while feeling that the artistry is that of the plasticine material itself, and not me, nevertheless I have a warm inner feeling of great creativity. I feel that I am outstripping Michelangelo and da Vinci combined.

One peculiarity of this Sistine Chapel phase is its great emphasis on detail of musculature. Once again, each statuesque figure grows in size until it becomes as large as the earth itself—but now the earth is that piece of statuary: a thousand-mile-long Michelangelo-type figure, and each elevation of contour of corrugated abdomen or delicately molded breast is a high ridge or mountain; each depression in the contour is a long valley; the delicately tinted veins are smoothly flowing rivers. It is an alabaster world, lovely to look at. . . .

This is a fleshy world. But it is not pleasant flesh, covered with skin. It is as flesh seen with the skin removed—and seen, too, as a microbe might see it from the inside: endlessly throbbing, endlessly pulsating, endlessly straining and striving. It is a world of huff and puff signifying nothing. It creates a feeling of vanity of vanities, all is vanity. It makes me feel as if these bodies, all flesh but without skin, were silently but painfully writhing and squirming in an eternal purgatory. The contrast with my alabaster world makes me think of *Paradise Lost*, with a totally unwanted purgatory gained. If the previous fantasies were Michelangelo and da Vinci, this is one of the dark all-pitying visions of Dante.

––––––––––

These lavish visions were seen with closed eyes. When the subject opened his eyes, the "movie" faded. He was as much an observer as a participant in the majestic phantasmagoria; the abundant creations hardly seemed to be his. The striking point is that these exuberant outpourings issued from a mind which had been almost unaware of the existence of such strange contents.

The schizophrenic hallucination, in contrast to LSD visions, is usually auditory, visual misperceptions occurring less frequently. A subcategory of schizophrenia, called oneirophrenia by Meduna, has perceptual phenomena similar to many LSD experiences. Hennell's account of his schizophrenic visions is illustrative:

As to the visioned creations, these were of finer, thinner stuff than iridescent bubbles, in all the details of their forms more minute and miraculous than anything upon earth. Indeed, they would have had little significance had they been such as could conceivably have been provided, or invented, from the experience of a human lifetime. There were small suns and strange twilight worlds of lakes and islands—not conceived as spinning balls, like our earth, but having definite yet changeable limits, as drops of oil which float on water. Planets, with their peculiar signs, came near, the sun was broken, and the face of the earth was changed, the landscape was never so enchanted. An ancient cave, passage, or hollow ladder, seemed to connect new earths; perhaps this was such as Jacob saw, for it was an image of remote antiquity.[2]

Sechehaye's patient remembered that the first evidence of her psychosis was an "illuminated vastness, brilliant light, and the gloss and smoothness of material things." The world of the insane she named "The land of intolerable glare." [3]

The delirium of head injuries, high fevers or drugs is also accompanied by hallucinations. The most common such state in the Western world is delirium tremens, the prerogative of the long-standing alcoholic. Its hallucinations are of either sight and sound and are commonly terrifying. Traditionally, small animals crawl over the walls and bedclothes. The DTs were compared with the LSDs by Ditman and Whittlesey, who found that DTs were predominantly characterized by hallucinations that were felt to be real and by anxiety, horror, depression, irritation and paranoid thoughts. The LSD experience, in contrast, was typified by euphoria, humor, relaxation and a nebulous sense of wonderment. Both groups reported perceptual distortions and the sensation of having an increased rate of thought.

One further type of hallucinatory activity ought to be mentioned because it points to an anatomic location. During neurosurgical operations on the brain conducted under local anesthesia, Wilder Penfield stimulated focal areas of the temporal lobe. Some of the patients reported clear and elaborate visions. If a song was recalled, all the associations connected with the musical piece were remembered with it, the places where it had been heard and the people who were there. The patient did not experience it as a memory, instead he believed that he was participating in the event. Simultaneously, he knew that he was lying in an operating room. Oddly enough, it did not seem incompatible to be in a hospital operating suite and also thousands of miles and many years away listening to the song. One way to obtain an hallucination, then, is to stimulate areas of the temporal lobe, The clinical counterpart of Penfield's work is found in temporal-lobe epilepsy due to a scar or tumor in this area. One of the symptoms consists of recurrent hallucinations of taste, hearing or vision which usher in the seizure.

We should be aware, however, of certain limits of the body and the mind. They are so fundamental that we are rarely conscious of them. To mention a few of the physical confinements: we are condemned to breathe every few seconds; the area between our shoulder blades will forever be invisible to us without the aid of a reflecting device; it is necessary to place portions of animals, plants, their by-products or their synthetic analogues into our mouths periodically. These are only a few of the many bodily limitations which we accept without question.

What are the limitations of the senses? We acknowledge that our sense organs are imperfect and restricted. We have no radar like the bat, no sonar like the dolphin. Dogs hear sound frequencies which we do not, and snakes sense changes in temperature far better than we. But by being able to build instruments which will do all these things and more, we have succeeded in extending our sensory boundaries enormously; beyond ultrasound and the electron microscope further extensions of the senses await us.

What are our psychic boundaries? Of what are we unaware? What is inconceivable? What information cannot be processed by us or our machines? These are unanswerable questions, but well within these confines, other strictures hem in the mind. Some of the barriers are our heritage, some our cultural endowment and some are the blockages of our personality. They comprise the innate assumptions of existence and the blinkers of the closed mind. Some examples: time is divided into a past, a present and a future; I can never be totally separated from myself; a thing cannot be its opposite. These mind-restricting assumptions are mentioned because in the hallucinogenic state they become less absolute, just as the incoherence of the mystic becomes more comprehensible.

The reduction of the ideational barriers by LSD permits certain kinds of creative activity. Adelson indicates that a direct connection exists between the ability to experience prelogical, primitive-archaic thinking and artistic creativity. It is not uncommon for artists to employ drugs to enter this state. But the intimate contact of the psychotic with his unconscious is not commonly accepted as creative. There is much more to creativity than accessibility to one's unconscious.

One possible definition of creative thinking is "an

unusual but appropriate solution to a problem." Novelty alone is not enough. The esoteric responses of the psychotic are not creative. Barron stresses that the creative person manages to fracture the perceptual constancies and the "averaging" function of his mind.

Whether LSD does or does not increase creativity remains an open question. No systematic research is available to help in finding an answer. One study by Berlin using a small number of artists found that the drawings showed an unusual expansiveness and relaxation of controls. Both color and line were freer and bolder, but the technical execution of the productions was impaired during the actual period of drug activity. The increased richness of imagery and inspiring thoughts, but difficulty in executing them, was also noted by us. Subject after subject spoke of highly esthetic experiences. "Constable was right, it is light falling on light," one said. Another: "I looked out the window into the infinitely splendid universe of a tiny mauve leaf performing a cosmic ballet."

Unique, strange and wonderful visions are accessible in the LSD state, but they must be carried over to a time when they can be set down. Numerous anecdotal reports are heard of the enhancement of creative activity in artistic individuals. Artists have stated that their styles changed as a result of their drug experience. They comment on the similarity between the LSD condition and the spontaneous creative feeling that they know during periods of inspiration. Another frequent comment is that the subject's appreciation for art or music has been either aroused or heightened. It would be surprising if an experience of great beauty and profundity, however attained, did not leave an unforgettable residue.

All that can be said at this time about the effect of LSD on the creative process is that a strong subjective feeling of creativeness accompanies many of the experiences. So far as I am aware, no instances of original solutions to scientific or mathematical problems have occurred. Certain individual artists may have become "unblocked" following their exposure. An increased esthetic appreciation of color, form, texture and sound persists. The evidence is scanty but provocative—the impression remains that promising methods may be developed which will assist in releasing potential talents. There is need of a proper study of original thinking and artistic creativity under LSD. Laboratory subjects superior in these qualities to the investigator himself may have to be used, for it would be futile to hope that such attributes can be implanted with LSD. Rather, the expectation that they might be augmented in talented individuals is more reasonable.

What has been said underlines the complexity of human mental function. Its very complexity has created additional levels of psychic activity, just as adding protons and electrons to an atom creates new elements with new properties. The simple neural pathways of the worm permit only stereotyped responses. Although its cellular composition is similar to the worm's, the human nervous system by virtue of its extraordinary intricacy has become capable of self-awareness, abstract thinking of a high order and those syntheses called inspirations. It would be narrow to believe that further elaborations are impossible. In the area of interpersonal transactions new levels of intensified empathic relationships seem to be evolving. As an example, phenomena now called "extrasensory" may be clarified one day and renamed "sensory."

We can delay the acquisition of such knowledge in two ways. One is by being completely closed to the probability that new concepts will supplant our current beliefs. The second is by being too precipitate in grasping every new and untested idea that arises.

6 *Model Psychosis or Instant Zen?*

Is the LSD state a model of madness, a touch of schizophrenia, or is it a short cut to *satori, nirvana* for the millions?

The first controversy about the hallucinogens in the medical literature was on another issue: whether a schizophrenic state or a toxic delirium was produced. For if schizophrenia could be reliably reproduced in the laboratory, a long step forward in its control would have been taken. If these drugs only caused a confused delirium, their value and interest would be minor, for deliriants are not particularly new or useful. In this argument a sort of compromise has been reached. It is generally agreed that the drugs do not exactly mimic schizophrenia, nor are they like the disorienting deliriants.

For at least ten years after LSD became available to clinicians, there was no question but that its administration inevitably produced a psychosis. Then reports from isolated groups insisted that something different than madness was being induced. In these circles the talk was of revelation, of great insights obtained, of feelings of profound unity and of experiences of self-transcendence. Even the illusions and hallucinations, instead of being terrifying and disorganizing, were described as pleasurable and meaningful.

It was mystifying to speak to one investigator who proclaimed that he had never seen anyone have a transcendent experience under LSD and then hear another assert that with the same dose 90 per cent of his subjects had positive, intensely gratifying nonpsychotic responses. Many researchers stated that none of their subjects could be persuaded to take LSD again for science or money; others insisted that their volunteers were eager to participate in future experiments. It almost seemed as though the investigators were talking about two entirely different drugs with completely opposite effects. Was it possible that out of the same bottle madness and supernal bliss could be poured?

The drug was indeed the same; the vast difference was in the divergent expectations and intent of the investigators. If LSD is given under disinterested laboratory conditions while impersonal assistants attach electrodes, take blood samples and perform a number of other puzzling tasks, and if the subject gets the impression that he will be temporarily mad and observers provide neither support nor reassurance, a psychotic state is bound to occur.

On the other hand, if the situation is a more relaxed

and agreeable one, if those in contact with the subject are sympathetic and understanding and if his own expectations are hopeful, he will probably go in a direction polar to madness. In both situations there are loss of ego controls, aberrant visions, altered mental activity and strong emotional changes. The first experience is a disorganization accompanied by horrendous anxiety, while the second is apprehended as organizing and valuable. These extreme differences tell us much about the wide traverse of the hallucinogenic drug effects. Naturally, many "in-between" reactions are seen, foothill rather than peak experiences, or lesser degrees of disorganization.

The modifying effects of the person and the place on the LSD experience are not unknown with other medicaments. From the same jug of whiskey come tears for one and laughter for another. As drink takes over the drinker, he is as liable to lose his sexual ardor as to develop lusty strivings.

The LSD state is, in essence, one of greatly heightened suggestibility, with environmental cues sensed most exquisitely. This sensitivity can assume extraordinary proportions, to the point where the observer's mind "can be read" from the minutest changes in tone, facial expression or posture. The loss of his customary defensiveness makes the subject much more responsive to these sensings. He responds, or overresponds, to the explicit or implicit signals of his associates with exaggerated mood swings.

It would be erroneous to imply that external structuring is the whole story. The direction that an LSD reaction takes is markedly dependent upon the make-up of the person who takes the drug. It is said that some Buddhist monks can go into *satori* while sitting on a dung heap with ashes strewn on their heads. In the same way, subjects who are open and accept the loss of their personality controls usually find the LSD encounter remarkable and worthwhile. No doubt some people will have a negative reaction under any circumstances because of their fears of self-surrender or because of an inflexibility of their defensive structure.

To the subject, of course, the two states of dissociation, the psychotic and the cosmic, have a vastly different significance. The divergent pathways that he can take are strongly determined by his interpretation and acceptance of the loss of self. If he becomes suspicious, doubtful or panicky, he is lost in a disruptive flux of meaningless turmoil. When the ego controls dissolve in a milieu of trust, the world within is glowing, serene and meaningful.

In order to judge whether LSD duplicates schizophrenia, something more should be said of the schizophrenic psychosis. This disorder, which afflicts one per cent of mankind, is thought to be caused by the childhood trauma of ambivalent, inconsistent parents. That a genetic predisposition to such a disruptive mental state exists is most likely. Maternal overprotection, or the perennial expression of conflicting attitudes, is presumed to prevent the child from learning satisfactory solutions to problems and to retard his emotional growth. Gregory Bateson calls the position of the pre-schizophrenic child a "double bind." The child is invariably faced with the impossible choice of defying mother or submitting and remaining a permanently immature, overdependent person. The social pressures and turmoil of adolescence and adulthood can induce a breakdown in such a tenuously adjusted individual.

The schizophrenic disorder can be examined on many levels. The biochemistry of schizophrenia is being researched all over the world, and although promising leads exist, no simple chemical answer to the disease is available at this time. Though many changes of a chemical nature are found, they may be the effects rather than the causes of schizophrenia.

The symptoms are varied, but many of the defects fall into a pattern. Reality is eventually rejected as unendurable, and a flight into metaphorical fantasy intervenes. Attention is turned inward to a splintered symbolism. The thinking process becomes tangential, unrealistic and bizarre. The schizophrenic is unable to abstract and in his conversations may respond to the sound or the association of words, rather than their meaning. His ability to separate external from internal events is defective—in other words, what is seen and what is remembered may be hardly distinguishable to him. He has difficulty ordering time into past, present and future. It is not surprising, in view of these defects, that his relationships with people suffer. He finds it perplexing to make sense of abstractions and customs, nor does he grasp the commonly agreed-upon cues of society. As a result, he is puzzled and suspicious and suffers from a lack of "play," or modulation of feel tone. The observer calls this flatness or inappropriateness of affect. It is appropriate only to his fragmented reality. He may be apathetic and withdrawn or terror-stricken and destructive, according to the content of his internal disorganization.

His hallucinations are usually auditory. The voices that he hears are protrusions of his own guilt and anxiety. They are often menacing or accusatory, but these may be converted into self-exalting voices expressing a hoped-for greatness. The delusional beliefs are closely tied to the hallucinatory productions.

It is interesting to note how timebound the delusional system of the paranoid schizophrenic can be. During the nineteenth century Napoleon was the prototype of the grandiose paranoid. Now he hardly ever makes an appearance. Hitler was the model for a while, but he is fading fast. Now, the Communists, the FBI and the atomic machines share the preoccupations of the deluded. In a theistic society the belief that one is God is a more enduring delusion that transcends the caprices of fashion.

When hallucinations of sight, taste, smell or touch occur, they too reflect the paranoid undercurrent. Suspiciousness is increased because the appearance of the outside world is so unfathomable. The schizophrenic does not see his world as we do ours. There is a gross flaw in the filtering, matching, and correlating of the sensory inflow, which some believe to be the primary defect. If the accurate computation of sensory information broke down, or if the normal overload of incoming data failed to be eliminated, a schizophrenic state certainly could result.

What is most likely is that a multiplicity of flaws contribute to the group of diseases called schizophrenia and that schizophrenia can have many causes in addition to those mentioned. Intolerable stress can temporarily make anyone psychotic. The "three-day schizophrenia" of World War II was seen in men with strong character structures who had to make life-and-death decisions under conditions of exhaustion, physical depletion and hopelessness.

In Table 2 (see Appendix B) some comparisons are made between an acute schizophrenic reaction, an acute delirial state, and some common features of the psychotic reaction that can develop with LSD. From the table it is evident that the psychiatrist or psychologist who experiences the hallucinogenic state can directly learn much about schizophrenic misperceptions. The actual experience of an hallucination, for example, adds dimensionality to one's understanding of a patient who is attempting to describe his. A firsthand knowledge of the fluidity and distortions of schizophrenic existence makes much of the behavior of the psychotic comprehensible and makes it easier to relate to him. McDonald has quoted from the report of a recovered schizophrenic:

> One of the most encouraging things that has happened to me in recent years was the discovery that I could talk to normal people who had had the experience of taking mescaline or lysergic acid, and they would accept the things I told them about my adventures [in schizophrenia] without asking stupid questions or withdrawing into a safe, smug

world of disbelief. Schizophrenia is a lonely illness and friends are of great importance. I have needed true friends to help me to believe in myself when I doubted my own mind, jolt me out of unrealistic ideas with their honesty, and teach me by their example how to work and play.[1]

Some LSD states are similar to some acute schizophrenic reactions, but important dissimilarities are also present. The LSD subject almost invariably retains the saving knowledge that what is happening is due to a drug and is temporary, whereas the acute schizophrenic cannot understand why everything has suddenly changed. Were LSD given without the subject's knowledge, the response would be much more overwhelming and anxiety-ridden. Schizophrenic character structure is notably inferior to that of the LSD subject, so that he can cope less effectively with the disorganized world. His distress is probably greater than that of his counterpart who has been made psychotic with LSD. Since it is technically not possible to maintain the drug-induced state for weeks because of the rapid onset of tolerance, it is not known whether a chronic LSD state could become more like schizophrenia.

One oddity about the effect of LSD on schizophrenic patients is that they can tolerate much larger amounts than nonschizophrenic subjects. Doses which ordinarily effect marked changes in normal people will do little to a chronic schizophrenic. Large amounts may reactivate the acute psychotic behavior or might induce symptoms which can be differentiated from the customary delusions and hallucinations. The implications of this fact are unclear. The psychotic could have a more effective metabolic system for destroying LSD because his metabolism is already actively engaged in dealing with another internal derangement of body chemistry. On the other hand, the effect may simply represent a part of the schizophrenic's over-all decreased responsivity to drugs. We might also assume that if he is already misinterpreting sensory information, it would take large amounts of LSD to make an appreciable difference in these distortions.

It is curious that the schizophrenic also endures sensory deprivation better than do normal individuals. Reportedly, many prefer the isolated state and even seem to benefit by it. Luby suggests that normal sensory inflow constitutes an overload for the schizophrenic and that his withdrawal represents an effort to reduce the input overload.

Something should also be mentioned about LSD's relation to such toxic psychoses as alcoholic delirium. Some of the resemblances and dissimilarities have already been noted in Table 2. Since delirium tremens is also transient, a comparison with the LSD psychosis is pertinent. The main difference is in the confusion that accompanies DTs. It is acknowledged that fearfulness is also frequently but not invariably present. One inebriate described his alcoholic hallucinations as "really interesting and entertaining, they kept me from getting bored during the week end in jail."

When we ask our recovering subjects whether they have ever known anything like the LSD condition before, an occasional one will say, "It's a little like when I was drunk." He mentions that some of the early symptoms, the numbness and unsteadiness, are reminiscent of alcoholic intoxication. He may point out that the feeling of not being responsible and in complete control of his thoughts is like the intoxicated condition. Then he usually goes on to say, "Even though being drunk is not really like LSD, how can I begin to describe it except in terms of something I have known, imperfect as the comparison is?" Such a response is understandable; a person who has never had any experience other than the drunken state might use that as the reference point to explain any other change from ordinary consciousness.

Certain LSD reactions can resemble any of the psychoses closely enough to be diagnostic problems when the examining psychiatrist is not informed that LSD has been administered. Tape recordings from selected LSD subjects and from acute schizophrenic patients were played to a number of psychiatrists by Hoffer. The listeners were unable to distinguish reliably between the two conditions. The debate about whether LSD brings forth a model psychosis is rather futile; undeniably, it can induce a model of psychosis, but for the reasons mentioned it cannot duplicate schizophrenia. A model need not reproduce every aspect of the thing modeled. For example, a model of a bridge, in addition to its difference in size, is also of different material and construction. Nevertheless, it is possible to learn much about the actual bridge from it. Just so, much can be

learned about schizophrenic symptoms from a study of
LSD phenomena.

The nature of the visionary experience must be
reviewed now so that an opinion about its relationship
to the LSD state is formulated. In addition, a theory of
the psychological basis of the visionary state will be
proposed.

The study of these transcendent episodes—we shall
call them religious, mystical, visionary or cosmic experiences without distinction—has been too long delayed
because of their connection with religion. Though it is
true that they form the core of many organized religions,
they nevertheless occur even more frequently outside
such settings. The attitude that these were too sacred,
that they were a part of theology, not of science, pre-
vailed. Psychiatry and psychology looked on them as
epiphenomena and were not inclined to deal with them.
It ought to be remembered that areas of research once
considered metaphysical have since come into the psychological fold. Visionary phenomena were also thought
to be so tenuous that a close scrutiny might shatter them
and a critical analysis could only destroy them. The
latter is partially true—the analysis of anything requires
its dissection. Still, much can be learned from the
components, and ideally a resynthesis becomes possible
at a later date.

Another common attitude toward important spiritual
or esthetic events is that once they are thoroughly
examined and understood, their intrinsic significance is
forever lost. On the contrary, an expert in acoustics may

enjoy Handel's *Solomon* more than we do; an anatomist comes to have greater appreciation and respect for the human body than those who know little about it; and the hummingbird's flight is no less wonderful when we have learned that its wings flutter 4,200 times a minute.

Let us assume that one day the religious experience will be redefined as a dys-synchrony of the reticular formation of the brain. Does this lessen its value to the individual and his society? What if it is discovered that by electrically stimulating a discrete area of the hypothalamus, a mysticlike event is produced? Olds has passed a weak current into specific hypothalamic points in the brains of mice, inducing a state more desirable to the hungry mouse than food; the thirsty animal would not stop pressing his self-stimulating bar to drink; the animal in heat would not desert the bar pressing even in the presence of a receptive mate. Whether this is the mouse equivalent of human bliss or ineffable rapture is, of course, unknown. But if the mystical state does come to have an anatomical location, will that diminish it? Its ethereal origin might be questioned, but the importance of its personal and interpersonal impact will still remain.

These matters are a proper and necessary subject for study. Knowledge about unsanity is of immediate and practical importance. The distinction between insanity and unsanity must be clarified. The unsane state is not solely a manifestation of the depleted, drugged, stressed mind. Maslow has found that it is the healthiest individuals who encounter peak moments most frequently. He suggests that in our emotional evolution the missing link between the anthropoid ape and mature man might be present-day man.

It must be made clear that a visionary experience, however attained, may have beneficial effects, adverse ones or none, whatever. It can be suppressed and forgotten, it can reinforce clandestine notions of grandiosity or it can "put a floor under me so that I can never again sink into complete aloneness and hopelessness." Actually, nothing is understood in detail, but the overall feeling of pure knowing pervades. It can, as will be seen, reshuffle the mazeway of doubt and depression. Old destructive patterns of behavior may suddenly be abandoned after an overpowering emotional experience. The learning of new attitudes and techniques may become easier in a posttranscendent period.

The varieties of visionary experience are great. Some are considered heavenly, some demonic; sometimes the divine and the devilish occur simultaneously. A few of their features, extracted from mystical and philosophic sources, are apparently to be found in every experience either in part or altogether.

The perceptual phenomena are the easiest to describe. Often a sudden, dazzling, brilliant light is seen. A visionary figure, generally a strange personage according to Aldous Huxley, may appear. If one is seen, it is interpreted within the context of one's personal beliefs. Ezekiel's visions are examples of these unfamiliar figures. The outer world is also strangely transfigured, color is intense, luminous and saturated, objects look fresh and radiant. What is looked at exclusively captures the attention and for that moment nothing else exists. The entire visual field is tunneled onto the percept itself. The intrinsic beauty and significance of the thing seen is enormously magnified to the beholder.

Self-identity is completely lost, and the self and that which is outside the self fuse. The ordinary subject-object relationships disappear, along with the conventional separateness of the external object. The extension of this egolessness can culminate in union or communion with the divine. St. Theresa, Ramakrishna, Meister Eckhart, St. John of the Cross and many others have described such momentary momentous occurrences.

Pervasive feelings of the "All rightness of the Universe" and a humble gratitude are the overwhelming emotional responses. There is a relaxation of tensions, the mood may be either one of vast serenity or an elated excitement. In retrospect, the emotional response is described as purgation (catharsis is the more modern word) to express the feeling of having been spiritually cleansed. Mystical pronouncements, previously obscure, become obvious. When the Upanishads say that "Atman [self] is all," the person who has lost his own ego boundaries and has flowed into the world outside is quite able to grasp the obscurity of the pronouncement.

These are very substantial alterations of the ego and its functions. It would be worthwhile to know how they come about. At present this knowledge is unavailable, but a hypothesis can be offered. The incident which evokes a spontaneous visionary experience may be an intense emotional, perceptual or even conceptual event. These can vary from deliberately sought-after experiences in contemplative meditation to unexpected "out of the blue" occurrences. Whatever their trigger, at least two psychological processes are evident. One consists of a marked reduction in the critical faculty; one's constant self-scrutiny and guardedness give way. A second is that the usual manner of processing incoming data alters; what previously was routinely registered and processed, now, for some reason, becomes a matter of prime attention. The focused ability to attend completely without the inhibitory effects of critical self-observation could lay the groundwork of a visionary experience.

Although differences do exist, the common resemblances of all unsane experiences are remarkable. When drugs induce such events, interesting parallelisms are also found. Sherwood, writing of the apparent universality of perception in the psychedelic, or drug-induced, transcendent experience, attributes the universal central perception to a single reality. An alternate explanation is just as likely. Once the mind is unhinged from sanity by whatever means, it can only go in a very limited number of directions. It can become delirious; it can convulse; it can become comatose; it can become psychotic; or it can become unsane. In each of these conditions there is heterogeneity, and yet in each a base of homogeneity. Unsanity being one of the final common pathways of the stressed mind, the varieties of its mental elaborations must of necessity overlap and contain a common core.

When we compare a description of the spontaneous visionary state with the psychedelic experience that may occur with LSD, the similarities are numerous and the dissimilarities few. The striking visual and emotional changes that have just been mentioned can also develop during the drug-induced condition. The only feature that is normally absent is the appearance of a visionary figure, and even this has occasionally been reported.

Alan Watts, who was originally doubtful, is now convinced of a close relationship between the natural and the drug-caused visionary state. Huxley is very positive about this point: "For an aspiring mystic to revert, in the present state of knowledge, to prolonged fasting and violent self-flagellation would be as senseless as it would be for an aspiring cook to behave like Charles Lamb's Chinaman, who burned down the house in order to roast a pig. Knowing as he does (or at least he can know, if he so desires) what are the chemical conditions of transcendental experience, the aspiring mystic should turn for technical help to the specialists. . . ." [2]

There remains a minority who disagree. It consists of individuals who have labored long and hard to achieve the state. For them it is incredible that without strenuous spiritual training and disciplined preparation such things are possible. The differences between the "easy" and the "hard" ways must be similar to the situation in which one man climbs the Zugspitze and another takes the ski lift. The view from the top is the same for both. The mountain climber has sweated and striven against the dangers. His view must be different from the ski-lift rider's because it incorporates the struggle and the triumph. Ski-lift transcendence can approach that of the mountain climber's only if the prior life preparation has also been one of training and self-discipline.

Others believe that the visionary experiences of the saints are devalued if they are equated to a chemical event and prefer to deny that they are in any way alike. Still others assert that everything that is not sanity must be insanity.

Despite the similarities, the spontaneous visionary experience must have a much greater impact upon the person. If it is the culmination of a long period of abnegation or strenuous mental exercises, the psychological stage has been set for the awesome event. When it strikes a man like a bolt out of the blue, the conviction that it has an otherworldly origin is great. The message it contains carries more certitude. The spontaneous experience is, therefore, more likely to produce lasting changes in the chosen person.

During the past decade the induction of transcendental states by means of drugs has been made more precise. The historical lessons of their religious use and the conditions necessary to achieve feelings of fellowship and communion have been partially clarified. Slotkin has surveyed the peyote cult in some detail. The vestigial psilocybe mushroom ceremony has demonstrated that certain simple devices tend to make for a sense of brotherhood among the communicants. Urban groups with the same goal report the use of similar practices.

First, the devotee must have faith in, or at least be open to the possibility of the "other state." His prior life experience and religious or philosophical beliefs may be helpful in preparing him for this openness. He must "let go," not offer too much resistance to losing his personal identity. The ability to surrender oneself is probably the most important operation of all. Van Dusen believes that the LSD *satori* comes only after the symbolic death of one's ego. An analytical, doubting attitude is incompatible with its achievement. A feeling of security and trust in the administrator is required. Assume for a moment that one is sitting on a sled at a summit looking down into a steep decline. Faith that the vehicle is durable and the driver expert can lead to an exhilarating experience. Doubts that it might disintegrate or that the driver is unequal to the situation will produce anxiety and dread.

Naturally a nonthreatening, pleasing environment will help procure the desired effect. Appropriate pictures and music have been employed to assist in the setting. Music is a particularly effective aid for this purpose. A certain aura of strangeness, but not too much (perhaps one standard deviation of strangeness) might be included.

The most important factor is the person or group who is present. If they are convinced of the value of the transcendent state, this conviction will be verbally or nonverbally transmitted. If they are negatively oriented toward such phenomena, it is likely that their feelings will influence the subject. When groups are foregathered for the purpose of self-transcendence, a summation of intergroup solidarity and suggestion can be powerful enough to procure it even with small amounts of the drug.

Finally the factor of dosage is relevant. Although small quantities (50 to 100 micrograms of LSD) are sufficient for susceptible individuals, the higher dosage levels (200 to 600 micrograms) are more certain in propelling the aspirant to the desired realm. It is presumed that when large amounts are used the individual is "pushed through," past any possible attempts at control. A recent innovation has been the use of certain stimulants, such as the amphetamines, in combination with LSD or psilocybin to enhance the probability of achieving the paradisiacal state.

It is interesting to observe in passing that the same elements of patient hopefulness, proper setting and therapist conviction are necessary prerequisites for all successful psychotherapies.

In order to demonstrate the relationships between the acute schizophrenic reaction and the visionary state, the stages of their development have been set down in tabular form (see Table 3, Appendix B). In addition, the five stages of inspiration are included because some gross resemblance to the other two conditions exists. The phenomenon of inspiration is not equivalent to the other two conditions, but it is interesting that the process follows a similar course.

All three processes consist of rapid alterations following problem-solving attempts. The inspiration produces a successful intellectual synthesis. The schizophrenic break results from the failure to resolve some stressful conflict, and all the psychic components are involved. A similar conflict may induce a visionary experience; in such instances the intense emotional experience may succeed in solving the problem. It must also be noted that these sudden and dramatic changes need not result in lasting transformations of personality or ideas—the individual may revert to his prior pattern of mental activity.

The original question: "Does LSD produce a model psychosis or a visionary state?" can now be answered by saying, "It does both," or more correctly, "It can do either." Huxley was not incorrect in indicating that it could be Heaven or Hell. Superficially, this may sound paradoxical, but perhaps the underlying relationships have been clarified in the discussion. LSD is like a trigger not only in the way it releases chemical activities that proceed long after the drug has been eliminated. It also seems to trigger a depth charge into the unconscious processes. The direction that the explosion will take is the result of factors other than the drug.

Now that the chemist has provided us with agents that peel away sanity, it is possible to discern an interesting juxtaposition of events. This is the era of man's psychic upheaval resulting from the products of his fertile mind. Rapid social movements tear at the cultural roots which once provided stability and faith. We have become a disbelieving society. Faith in the old answers to the questions of life and death is losing ground, and the new rational explanations are no comfort. Under the pressure of this grinding dilemma, the regression of a few into creeds and cults which seem to have no more validity than fealty to Zeus is a despairing response to the existential emptiness. Others encapsulate the spiritual failure in some remote crypt of the mind. Still others believe—without belief.

Strangely enough, for some persons these drugs do

have the ability to compose the universe. For once its meaning is wholly felt—not thought out. That so anti-intellectual a product should have been fabricated in our highly intellectualized civilization is the cream of the jest.

7 *Debriefings*

The person who has not taken one of the hallucinogenic drugs or experienced a similar state without chemical assistance may not have been brought much closer to an understanding of it by the foregoing attempt at an explanation of the nature of the condition. In this chapter the reports of people who volunteered to take LSD for a research project may convey the LSD state better than any efforts to analyze it. If they seem well written, this perhaps speaks for the creative potential of the LSD state. The narrations were set down shortly after the test ended, usually that same evening. A deliberate attempt has been made to extract both "good" and "bad" reports so that the whole spectrum of possible reaction forms can be scanned. The reports will speak for themselves; only brief comments have been added when some point seems to require elaboration.

Everyone who has studied the LSD state has been impressed by the way factors apart from the drug itself modify it. Some of the more important variables are the personality of the individual, his current life situation, the attitude of those in contact with him during the experience, the setting and the reasons why the drug was taken and given. Therefore, something will be said of these matters.

The setting of the test was a rather drab hospital room. The investigator's motives were to study the psychological changes that evolved during the period of drug activity. The subjects' reasons for volunteering varied from curiosity, a hope that they might get to know themselves a little better, to a desire, among the professionals, to understand what their patients were feeling. Many of the unpaid volunteers were doctors, nurses, psychologists and attendants. Secretaries, teachers, businessmen and housewives made up the rest of the group. The attitude of the observer was friendly, sincere and supportive.

At the height of the reaction the subjects were given the same series of psychological tests they had received before the experiment. Since some of the tests are mentioned in the reports, they will be briefly explained. The Rorschach consists of ten cards designed to allow the subject to project his own associations onto amorphous ink blots. The Sentence Completion test has a series of open-ended statements, as: "I pleased my friends when . . ." or "My mother should have. . . ." Word-association tests contain lists of words to which the subject is supposed to respond with the first word that comes to mind. The Shipley-Hartford is the test of intelligence used in this study. Part of it is a multiple-choice vocabulary test, the remainder taps abstract think-

ing with such items as "Two = w; four = r; one = o;
three = ?" The TAT, or Thematic Apperception Test,
is a series of pictures on cards about which the subject is
supposed to make up a story. The Bender Gestalt cards
consist of ten rather simple geometrical figures that are
supposed to be reproduced after the card has been taken
away. The Draw-A-Person test simply requires the subject to draw a person, and then one of the opposite sex.
Finally, the adjective check list is a series of such words
as "tense" and "happy," which are checked when they
correspond to the current mood of the subject.

On the morning of the experiment the subject arrived
at the hospital without having had breakfast and was
given a colorless, tasteless glass of water. He could not be
sure that LSD was in the fluid, for he understood that
sometimes placebos were given.

Now, to the stories of the subjects themselves. The
first is from a doctor.

I was not particularly apprehensive about undergoing
the test since I was well aware that the changes produced were temporary and that the possibility of complications was negligible. I wondered what sort of a
reaction I would have; I had read that a number of
people have a painful catatonic withdrawal, others a
tormented depressive state. I fancied that I would be a
catatonic.

After a half hour I suggested that the LSD would
probably have no effect.

One hour after drinking the water I knew that I had
taken a potent drug. The first change was one of plea-

sant relaxation. As the morning wore on, this sense of tranquility increased to an undescribable mood of great calm and peace. The problems and strivings, the worries and frustrations of everyday life vanished; in their place was a majestic, sunlit, heavenly inner quietude. This was a pure mood change. True, there were fantasies of floating or standing on a high place looking at range after range of mountains recede in the distance, or of walking under high vaulted arches in a secluded garden, but these were transient. As I recall now, the peace was within and my reveries only embellished this monolithic theme. Neither alcohol nor any other drug had done this to me.

I seemed to have finally arrived at the contemplation of the eternal truth, all else was long since gone. The solitude of this place did not disturb me, I would have preferred to remain forever in this "Nirvana without the ecstasy."

This was the basic and most impressive mood change. This made the unpleasant side effects of the drug more than tolerable. The physiological changes were also of interest to me professionally. First I was aware of a numbness; this was followed by shivering and later by a transient feeling of intense cold which required three blankets to partially overcome. Slight tingling of the fingers was noted briefly. The shaking and shivering was so great at its height that it produced abdominal tenseness. I recalled having this tightness of the abdominal musculature in the past and it was usually associated with anxiety. I was interested to find that despite the generalized tremulousness and the abdominal tenseness no anxiety was experienced.

I soon discovered that by closing my eyes, an increase in the intensity of the languid, peaceful feeling would occur, and that opening my eyes or listening to a voice would bring me back to reality, especially if I tried. This peculiar change in contact depending on the impinging stimuli was fascinating. At one moment I was a timeless spirit, but I only needed to open my eyes to be able to make some trivial comment. Needless to say, I was soon reluctant to interrupt my delicious fantasy with human trivia.

I could also discern a waxing and waning of the emotional and physiological effects of the drug. They built up to a peak and diminished back to the base line. This wavelike effect was marked during the entire period.

One of the grossest distortions was that of time perception. Centuries were lived, yet the minute hand of the watch barely moved. My Rorschach took 200 light years,* the longest on record.

Misperceptions of space were minor. I can recall only one incident. We left the test room and went into the corridor. The hall had shrunk since I had last seen it that morning, and the perspective as I looked down to the end was so exaggerated that I would have had to crawl through the distant end. This was especially true since I was now some nine feet tall.

Sounds seemed more hollow and closer to the ear than they really were. There were no auditory halluci-

---

* It is admitted that a light year is a measurement of distance, not of time, but this is how it was written.

nations. My visual hallucinations were not important and were sort of disappointing. I had heard of the vivid colored imagery seen by others. I could only create a few pastel shades at the edges of objects and, only briefly, a multicolored mosaic on the ceiling. For a while the ceiling rippled like a pond, but I knew it was an hallucination and knew that it really wasn't rippling. One distinct color misperception occurred on Card V of the Rorschach. When I picked it up there were gleaming flecks of gold shining almost dazzlingly. I was familiar with the card and I knew that it was black-gray on white, yet there it was spattered with gold to my surprise. At that point I didn't know that it was a hallucination, and it puzzled me but I didn't get paranoid about it.

Actually, my paranoidal feelings were minor (in my estimation). I trusted those around me, and there was only one occasion when I felt even mildly suspicious. It occurred when I happened to look out the window and saw the old canteen being demolished. Only the day previously I had asked someone what they were going to do with the canteen. Now it was being torn down. Why? What could this mean?

My Rorschach responses were quite different from what I would have given ordinarily. Even I could see that they were "sick," but I didn't care at that point. While looking at some of the cards the shadings suddenly became very meaningful and would stand out like a relief map, and the various tones of gray rather than the outline determined the response.

Despite my omnipotent position in Valhalla, I did

poorly on the Bender and the Shipley-Hartford. My remarks probably were much less than brilliant. I rambled and stopped in midsentence. I realized I was silly, and that my wit was of poor quality.

The great problem was one of communication. It was impossible for me to describe what I felt, first, because words were inadequate, second, because the languor and reticence to interrupt the experience was so great.

I would think that no one is aggressive under LSD. The feeling of passivity that I had was overwhelming. There was no disorientation; substantial mental confusion was limited to a few moments. Unfortunately, there were no erotic fantasies.

When lunchtime arrived and food was offered, I became aware of a complete disinterest in food. Food was for earthlings; in my land there were no appetites. Finally I was persuaded to eat something and it tasted marvelously good. When I looked at what I was eating and saw that it was two pieces of dry white bread, a slice of bologna and some droopy lettuce, I realized that I was still under the influence.

I wonder whether much of the LSD experience is not dependent on the surrounding situation. Nevertheless the basic mood reaction must be characteristic for the individual. I feel sure that repeating the test would permit a return to that High Place where all is serenity.

After I had returned to my old, very ordinary, self a few things bothered me. One was that I could not remember enough of that unique experience. Another was that somewhere I had read a description of the place I had been. I thought I knew, and looking it up,

III

sure enough, DeQuincey had been there a hundred years ago. "For it seemed to me, as if then, first I stood at a distance and aloof from the uproar of life: as if the tumult, the fever and the strife were suspended; a respite granted from the secret burdens of the heart; a Sabbath of repose: a resting from human labors. Here were the hopes which blossom in the paths of life; reconciled with the peace which is in the grave; motions of the intellect as unwearied as the heavens, yet for all anxieties a halcyon calm; a tranquility that seemed no product of inertia, but as if resulting from mighty and equal antagonisms; infinite activities, infinite repose."

———

Despite the expectation that he would enter a catatonic state of withdrawal and muteness (his exposure occurred ten years ago, when the literature generally spoke of the LSD reaction as a "model psychosis"), the subject actually felt a notable, clear-headed tranquility. One's expectations are not always confirmed. His comments about the waxing and waning of the effects are almost universally heard. This undulation correlates with no known biologic rhythm, and its explanation is not yet available.

A full-blown catatonic reaction did occur in a psychologist who was ordinarily bright and friendly. For most of the day she was mute and immobile. It would have been difficult for a psychiatrist who did not know her to pick her out of a room full of female catatonic schizophrenics. The changes in her psychological tests reflected a regression from a high level of operational efficiency to one of disorganization and withdrawal. Her clear report is a valuable description of what it might feel like to be a schizophrenic with many catatonic features.

I had an immediate feeling of relief after taking the LSD. The apprehension which I had felt earlier was almost, though not completely, knocked out. The deed was done, and I was extremely curious about what would happen. I had a very definite set of expectations. First I expected to feel as if I had had about eight martinis and to act happy drunk as I ordinarily would; I expected a lot of interesting color effects; I thought I would have vivid and entertaining (even if frightening) visual hallucinations; sooner or later I expected that I might become catatonic in appearance while I enjoyed my hallucinations in private.

When the psychologist first asked how things looked to me, I had not noticed anything; but then I saw that the room was not quite in focus, but not badly. It was as if I had not had my glasses on. He asked me some questions which I answered but didn't pay much attention to, because I was more interested in seeing what things looked like. Then I noticed that I had made a noise with my teeth which I could hear extremely clearly. This intrigued me, and I tried rubbing my teeth together in different ways—gently, hard, and listening to my teeth, and I discovered I could stop it only with very great effort. Some noises outside the room (explained as a floor polisher) buzzed so loud I couldn't hear my teeth, and I felt that I couldn't stand it if the buzz didn't stop. The momentary rage which I felt then was the last clearcut feeling that I had for quite a while. . . .

The psychologist told me to get up and go over to a table and take some tests. I started to go but nothing happened. I tried very hard to move. I pushed, but my body would not move. When I finally got it going, it went all right but it was hard to stop. I wasn't thinking about anything but what I had to do, which was move. I had a test in front of me which I had to do. It was hard. It didn't occur to me (then or at any time later on) to refuse to do it. I had to push to move my hand and put out an awful lot of effort for very little return. The pencil felt very strange in my hand, almost as if I were not holding it at all, it was just there. Nothing had very much to do with me. I felt quite frustrated while I was pushing without any result. Sometimes I would find myself moving the pencil around and around in a dot, and a lot of effort would be required to stop. Sometimes I would notice painful sensations in some part of my body which I knew in a vague sort of way were caused from being in one position too long. When I felt these I knew they were intense sensations, but it didn't seem to matter very much. Whenever I became aware of pain, I tried to change position to relieve it. Sometimes it worked, and I was able to move. Sometimes I tried my best for a long time and nothing happened, so I would just stay the way I was and put up with the pain until I didn't notice it any more.

People would come in from time to time. If they were within my field of vision, I saw them. If they were not within my field of vision, I forgot they were there. Once I seemed to clear up a little, and I wondered who was sitting next to me; I tried to turn my head to see, but it wouldn't move. Whenever anybody asked me something, I tried to answer. Sometimes I wouldn't be thinking at all, just blank. Occasionally I would know exactly what I wanted to say. I would try to say it, and nothing would come out. Then I would line up some words to say, line them up in my mouth and work on getting the first one out on the theory that if I could get one word out, the rest would be easy. But this usually did not work. Sometimes I would try to boil down a complicated thought to one word which I had some chance of being able to get out. Sometimes I couldn't come up with anything so any word would do. Somebody asked me if I were happy. In a fuzzy sort of way I wanted to explain that I just couldn't answer the question because it didn't have any meaning. I didn't think I was happy or unhappy. I wasn't sure just what these were. The terms were just not relevant. This thought was hopelessly complicated to me. To get out of not being able to say anything, I just said "Sure." I existed moment by moment, with no thought beyond the current moment. I did not have any hallucinations or any bizarre thoughts. There was just nothing. Later I thought of this as an almost complete absence of imagination, curiosity, capacity for feeling, interest in anything; all that was left was existence at the moment, and even that was hopelessly complicated.

For most of the morning I wanted a cigarette but couldn't do anything about it. When I was finally given one, this was good, but I didn't get any satisfaction out of it. I spent most of lunchtime trying to knock the ashes off, and I felt extreme frustration at having what I wanted in my hand and not being able to do anything about it no matter how hard I pushed. Sometimes I did not know whether I had a cigarette in my hand or not, and I wondered idly if I would burn myself or if I would notice if I did. Once, while walking, I realized that I was coming to some steps and if I didn't get my eyes where they could look I would hurt myself. This didn't concern me especially, but I worked on myself and on turning my head down so that my eyes could see down. When I was level again, I knew that my eyes were still down; but there wasn't any reason for them to be up, so I didn't put myself through the work involved in getting them up.

When I took the Rorschach there was just nothing there. I tried very hard to find something to say, but there was just very little there to be said. Only Card VIII was definitely something. I wanted to say "Squirrels," and I tried a long time but I couldn't get the word out. Finally, I gave up and decided to try "Animals." Before I had worked on that word very long, I figured out vaguely that "Animals" wouldn't do because then the psychologist would ask me what kind, and I would have to say "Squirrels," and I just couldn't. So I said "Bears." They didn't look like bears but it was better to say "Bears" than not say "Squirrels." If a lack of feeling can be a feeling, I felt this very keenly throughout the Rorschach because there was just nothing on the inkblots.

Most of the time I did not feel any desires of any kind except to have a cigarette, go to the bathroom and succeed in getting through the job of the moment. I was aware of needing to urinate for a long time, and I hoped I would be able to do something about it before I made a mess, but this really didn't concern me very much. The desire to do the job of the moment was not really a felt desire, but more a lack of choice; the idea of not doing it just did not occur to me, and when I tried to do something, not being able to do it was frustrating.

The job had to be very clearly defined before I had any chance of doing it. For example, when asked to draw a person, the psychologist gave me instructions enough only for the head. Then I was blocked. When it turned into a question mark, I knew that wasn't a person, so I tried again. I tried to stop the next one from turning into a question mark but I couldn't. The next one I made very small so I wouldn't have to move much and would be able to finish it before it turned into a question mark. I boxed it in because I had done it and it was not a question mark. Then, when I had to draw another figure, I already knew how to keep from making question marks, so it was a little easier. I boxed it in good because I knew I wouldn't have to do any more and this one would never be a question mark. Then the psychologist asked me what sex, which had not occurred to me, and since he had not given me anything to choose from, I just made another question mark which seemed to be a perfectly adequate answer.

When I took the Sentence Completion, I started

writing "Nothing" because it fit. After a while I saw that I had put in quite a few "Nothings," and I realized that I was no longer reading the sentences. Instead I was listening to the sound the pencil made as I automatically wrote "Nothing." It sounded very much like my teeth. I tried to stop perseverating "Nothing," and I wrote something else on the top of the next page, "No." Then I was listening to the pencil again. So I tried to write "No" only where it seemed to fit, since I couldn't come up with any other word. This left a lot of blanks. I was aware that I hadn't finished this job and I would probably still be working at it if the paper had not been taken away from me.

Later, when I got a couple of sentences out, this seemed to make everything so much easier, and I began to be able to say words fairly well, and to come out of the drug quickly. During this period I saw some clear well-rounded images coming out from a shiny spot on the wall—all sorts of people, animals, horsemen, etc. Seeing these also helped me get interested in what was going on around me. After I came out of it, I still would occasionally catch myself in an awkward position with some part of me becoming numb, and I would have no memory of having been in that position.

My most striking impression of the way I felt was of the tremendous amount of effort I was putting out for very little return. Now it seems to me that I found everything impossible but unavoidable. I felt no anxiety at any time after the drug took effect. I think now that anxiety would have been a very pleasant feeling and a

welcome relief from the nothing in which I spent
today.

———

"It was a naughtmare," she said a few days after
recovery. Awareness had been retained during the experience, but it was very constricted. Thinking, feeling
and the ability to perform had contracted to almost
nothing. Like a true catatonic, she maintained uncomfortable, even painful body positions for long periods.
Some catatonic schizophrenics who have recovered can
remember that during their illness they were aware of
what was going on around them even though they might
have appeared to be completely out of this world.

A sensitive, introspective hospital physiotherapist appeared relaxed and happy, undisturbed by the loss of his
usual controls and defenses and the appearance of
repressed material. A portion of his report follows.

It is now 10:00 P.M. and this will be an effort to
narrate what has happened to me since 8:00 A.M. today.
I feel as though something must still happen; that just
being permitted to see isn't enough; that just understanding better isn't enough; that there must be a
definite act on my part, a concrete, palpable attempt to
describe what I felt, am feeling, will feel. And I hope,
but I'm not at all certain, that I can do better than my
"clear confusion" of this afternoon. I wonder what
would have happened this morning if you took me out
to play tennis. Once upon a time I devoted a lot of time

to this game but never got much better than mediocre high school varsity. I watched the greats of my time: Tilden, Johnson, LaCosta, Borotra, and tried to do as they did—unsuccessfully. I think, this morning, for a while I might have been able to hit a ball as hard as Tilden, with the precision of LaCosta, the dedication of little Bill Johnson and with the sheer, undiluted joy of movement of Borotra.

I said this all started this morning at 8:00, but, of course it didn't. It started some place in the distant past, millions of years ago, before we measured time on watches. It started someplace before there was language to juggle and make games with. It started before we learned to thrust and parry with words. It started when the early man could only express himself in the inarticulate, guttural, "ghoos" and "ghahs" of an infant—when his fellow man could only understand by understanding. Back there someplace, this started, this hard core of a desire to be—became. Call it by any name. I tried earlier today to describe it. I can't now, but I can try. Your faces and bodies were changing forms, but this did not seem too strange to me. Your face colors changed, but that was not disturbing. I was at different times suspicious of you both, and I will never again belittle a patient's anxieties. I know now that nothing was contrived, except perhaps some superficial movements calculated to irritate me, but it is quite clear to me now that the slightest movement, the change in voices, a curtain waving in a breeze, assumes many values. One thing is quite clear to me now as I return to the changing pictures, the colors swimming, retreating, changing; these colors to an artist are in reality a picture frame. The hard core, the soul, the God, the Be of the artist is the picture. His genius is as great as his ability to put his Be or Is or Oneness on the canvas. This can be rewritten for any of the arts. My own slant was, I believe, particularly toward form and movement.

At one point when I persisted in holding onto a single hair as if that was all that held me to reality, and perhaps it was, you said "Why not choose a speck on the floor?" I tried very hard to tell you it couldn't be just a "speck on the floor." It had to be a symbol of my choice, and this now seems logical to me. You tell me that I cannot see through a file card—see the blood vessels in my hand—see the thickness of printers' ink—and I must bow my head and say it can't be done. But surely, I did it. It is just not logic. What makes our logic better than the psychotics' logic?

Now, I felt this fine little hair. I could measure it. I could describe the colors of this delicate tube. I could let it float between my fingers and it became a ballet dancer or a Chinese horse—not as realities, but with all the grace and form. I was, at the time, an instrument that could measure the diameter of the hair, I could weigh it—and these were realities. And so we approach the next thing that I do not understand yet. Perhaps when fear goes I will do better. Some place in this there was an element of death. About as close as I ever have been or will be, I suppose, without actual death. Again, let me humbly try. Once I damn near drowned, but that was a fighting struggle to stay alive. It wasn't this. "Farewell is a little death"—not this. In an undiluted sexual consummation there must be a little death, but not like today's. Perhaps like this: I don't remember the detail but during the drawing of the geometric figures I said that it would have been better not to complete the figure because there would remain a "might have been," and I slid this paper, that beautifully textured paper, over the side of the desk. This falling off, but the ability to come back, this incompleteness, this might-be-ness is a little bit more like it. Some nine years ago my mother had a coronary along with the usual family hysteria, so undignified at such a moment. Well, she was able to speak to me shortly thereafter when the pain had been alleviated. "It was so nice and peaceful," she told me. "Why did you bring me back?" This is how close I was or even closer, but with the ability to see myself.

———

The remark that somehow there was something of death in the experience has been repeated many times. Ordinarily, the tension that is mobilized when we think consequentially of our personal death results in suppression, denial or some other defensive maneuver. Under LSD the concept of death may not be threatening at all; it can be looked at squarely and scrutinized with equanimity.

What this subject appears to describe is a primordial emotional state where subject-object relationships no longer exist and one is a part of, not apart from, one's environment.

He was given a second dose of LSD two months later, to examine the changes that might occur when the initial apprehension of taking a potentially threatening drug were not present. Here is his comparison of the two episodes:

> Yesterday, at some point, I was asked how this LSD experience compared with the prior one, a reasonable question. How can I give a reasonable answer? Last March I was at no loss for words. It seemed of the greatest urgency that I relate and narrate and retell. Today I am reluctant to talk or write. This experience was very different. The first time it was an adventure in entirely new audio-visual sensations, three-dimensional and techni-color. I traveled a road I had never been on before, a fast, furious ride, during which I twisted and turned to see and hear everything possible. The same road was traveled yesterday, but this time I went a bit slower. Oh, I saw the old sights, recognized them and went on, seeking the things I might have missed on the first trip. And since I was riding more slowly, I had time to look a little longer and a little deeper into myself, since the road was me. This trip was, perhaps, less perceptive but more conceptive.

A remark made by those who have taken mescaline or LSD more than once is that a transition in the nature of the reaction occurs. Preoccupation with color and dimension may fade, and one is likely to have more of an internal experience. Nor is there any guarantee that it may not become painful or terrifying. On the other hand, first experiences that were very uncomfortable can be followed by pleasurable ones on a second occasion.

A young resident physician in psychiatry, who was apparently quite concerned with what he would be like with his defenses down, supplied the following story:

Before I took the lysergic acid I was convinced that I would have a paranoid reaction. I was not sure in my own mind whether this would be of a fearful or of a highly hostile, suspicious nature. The only thing I knew about lysergic acid was that it "made people crazy."

I had seen a movie of a subject who had taken lysergic acid. This particular man, an artist, became quite friendly and was in what I could best describe as an ecstasy. However, I was certain I would not have such a pleasant reaction. My emotion prior to swallowing the medication was predominantly apprehensive and fearful. I was afraid that some of my actions while under the drug would indicate some marked personality fault or disorder. I was also afraid of losing control of myself, and I was especially afraid of hostile, destructive behavior.

Just after taking lysergic acid, the doctor suggested that possibly I had received a placebo. I doubted that this was so because of the work and effort involved in seeing a subject go through the process. However, it did make me resolve to fight harder to control myself. To have been suggested into a reaction would, to me at least, be quite shameful.

About fifteen minutes after drinking the 100 micrograms of lysergic acid, I began to feel quite lightheaded. The feeling was very much like that which one has when recovering from a faint. For a few minutes I felt as if I were going to be sick to my stomach and finally I felt that I was about to pass out. I fought this feeling to the best of my ability. Probably because I had always found that activity reduced this light-headedness, I began to pace the floor. While it was suggested that I not struggle against it but that I close my eyes, I laughed and said I wasn't going to be trapped into this. By this time my bladder was quite full and I went to the bathroom. As soon as I left the room in which the tests were given I felt that I had to pull myself together, since this was a hospital and I was a doctor. I felt that I had to put on my suit coat and to straighten my tie and maintain at least some form of dignity. Interestingly enough, this feeling remained throughout the entire test.

On one occasion I felt like hitting the wall with my fist. I did this and was quite surprised when I felt no pain at all. As the feeling of light-headedness increased, I began to become more fearful. Suddenly I felt quite frightened. I felt almost as if I were going under or dying. I was just about to ask if I couldn't have the antidote and come out of it when it was suggested that I begin to take the psychological tests. When I sat down to take the tests I immediately felt a little better. However, I found that I was unable to really make the pencil go where I wanted it to go. It almost seemed as if my hand belonged to someone else.

Suddenly the light coming through the window began to attract me. I stopped taking the test and stared out the window. By this time it seemed as if several hours or possibly days or even a year or more had gone by. I looked at my watch and realized that it had only been fifteen minutes since I had gone down the hall to the bathroom.

In spite of the fact that I could not see quite clearly, everything seemed somehow wonderful to me. The grass outside was the greenest I had ever seen. I had a funny feeling that I wanted to run across the lawn and play. The sun and the day felt warm and wonderful. The light sparkling from the cars was as beautiful as anything I had ever seen. Under a palm tree on the lawn immediately in front of the building there was a red lawn chair. I found this red color just about the most beautiful thing I had ever seen. The way it combined with the shadow and the light seemed to me to be one of the most beautiful things that I had a chance to see.

I had a strange feeling that somehow I was making up everything beyond the parking lot. However, when I later recovered from the drug I found out that what I had seen actually did exist. There was a strange feeling of everything being somehow unreal or not really there. Interestingly enough, this was not frightening but rather a pleasant feeling. Although initially I had no positive feelings toward the psychologist, I began to feel quite friendly and warm toward him.

It was about this time that the psychologist suggested that he shut the blinds so I could concentrate on the tests. I had the feeling that I would have cheerfully killed him if he had done so, provided I could work up enough energy to do this. The strange thing was that there was really no feeling of hostility in this but rather one of simply removing an unpleasant object. This feeling of wanting to be rid of the nuisance did not seem to interfere in any way with the warm comradeship I felt for him at the moment. It was almost as though he no longer existed as a person but only as something that I felt warmly toward.

Suddenly the entire situation seemed even nicer. It was as if all the warm, sunny, wonderful days of my childhood had been rolled into one, and this was the day. I felt like a child looking out of the window at the beautiful, beautiful world. Never in all of my life have I seen anything that looked as beautiful as this particular day. Even simple things like a red necktie or that red lawn chair seemed absolutely wonderful. This is especially interesting in view of the fact that I knew I had had lysergic acid, and this was an experiment, and I was aware that things would not stay like this forever. Nothing seemed very important to me and I had a strange feeling that if I felt like it I could just step out of the window. I knew that I would fall and probably be killed but this didn't particularly bother me. At the same time I had no intention of trying it. At this point I began to feel that I could die very cheerfully, that, in fact, it wouldn't bother me at all to be eaten by lions just like the early Christians. Time began to have no beginning and no end, at times it seemed to move very rapidly, at other times extremely slowly. However, whenever I looked at my watch I was always amazed that so little time had passed.

I had the feeling that I knew what the purpose and the reason for life was. The feelings that I had at the time could not be very well described in psychiatric terms but best described in either religious or poetic ones. I had a very strong feeling that everyone was basically good, and that once the defenses and the garbage, so to speak, that we pick up throughout our lives were stripped off, that there really was such a thing as the brotherhood of man. . . .

The psychologist kept insisting that I take the tests and I refused to do this. At the time I refused I was not in the least aware that I was unable to take the tests. In fact, even now I have the feeling that I could have done them. Somehow, though, they were not interesting to me and I couldn't keep my mind on them. I had never felt this wonderful before and I would never feel this wonderful again. It was my intention to enjoy it and to hell with the tests.

The doctor came into the room. He asked me if I would like to take a walk. I had the feeling that he really understood how I felt at this moment. I was very anxious to go and yet at the same time I was quite afraid that I would make a complete ass of myself in public. I somehow seemed to know that I was quite safe in this room and quite safe saying anything I wanted to either of them, but that outside of the room I had to watch my behavior. The hallway seemed dark and gloomy to me. It also had a sobering effect on me. It reminded me again even more forcibly that this was a hospital, that I was a doctor here and that I had to maintain some sort of dignity. I also remember hating to leave the warmth and sunshine of that room. . . .

Lunch was probably the best lunch I've ever eaten in my entire life. Somehow food tasted at least a thousand times better. I remember eating, or at least thinking I was eating, very slowly and savoring each bite and each sip. As I ate I also began to feel that I was beginning to slip out of this wonderful mood that I was in. I had no desire to do this and, in fact, would have refused to take the antidote if it had been offered me.

As this mood gradually left me it was like coming out of a beautiful valley and watching the fog or the mist block it off behind you. I felt a great deal of regret at having the effects of the lysergic acid wear off. At the same time I was immensely grateful that I was able to have this experience. I have no particular desire to repeat it, at least at the present time. Although my memory is gradually fading, I have felt much more comfortable since the test than I did before. Somehow I was rather surprised when I found out that under lysergic acid I was really a rather nice, warm sort of a person. The other feeling I retain is that no matter how bad things get I always have a nice, comfortable, warm, happy place to go. The feeling is almost as if I carried a quiet, pleasant, serene garden around inside of my head. At times, even now, I can shut my eyes and get back a weak approximation of the feelings I had then. Up until the present time my dreams at night have shown an interesting change; before the lysergic acid I would have at least one and probably more anxiety-type dreams during the night. Following the tests and up until the present time all the dreams have been rather childishly pleasant, quite simply of a wish fulfillment type. It is almost as if the dreams were not censored, or indeed, as if there were no need of a censor. Last night, however, I again had one dream in which anxiety played a part. However, the anxiety involved in this dream was rather limited and bothered me neither at the time I was dreaming nor later when I woke up.

In general the feelings that I noticed while under the influence of LSD were as follows. One of the most noticeable was that the world was somehow one vast, friendly, warm, protecting unit. I felt that everyone was my friend or that at least their inner self, the core, so to speak, when stripped of all its armorplate and hostility, would be friendly. The other feeling noted was that although my actual vision was not as good as normal, everything that I perceived seemed much more beautiful, much brighter, much more alive, much warmer than it normally would be. I felt neither guilt nor hostility at the time and that it was really impossible to become very angry at anyone. I also felt that somehow I knew and could perceive the truth better than anyone else. This truth that I felt seemed to be that underneath everyone is a pretty nice person and that somehow they are all related to one another in the sense that there is some sort of a thread or a thought or some sort of tie between each person's inner self or soul or what have you.

From an intellectual point of view I feel that this experience was valuable insofar as it helps me understand what patients must feel. There is an immense amount of effort that is required to do even a simple task such as to walk or to make a simple line of drawing. It should enable me to become much more patient and understanding than I ever have been before. I think it has taken away my feelings that the patients were at times malingering.

———

A number of items in this report bear elaboration. The subject hit the wall with his fist yet felt no pain. Others have also remarked on this decrease of pain perception, and systematic studies have demonstrated an increase in tolerance of pain.

Despite the very profound changes engendered by the drug, this physician was well aware of his situation throughout the experiment. He knew that he had to maintain some sort of professional dignity and was able to pull himself together and perform adequately when it became necessary. Neither his sense of the social amenities nor his awareness of himself and how he should behave was impaired.

The discovery that underneath the mask he presented to the world lay "a nice guy" was surprising and gratifying. Instead of the expected underlying aggression, suspiciousness and anger, warmth and friendliness came forth. Indeed, one wonders whether our animal heritage may not be derived as much from the animals who came in peace to drink at the water hole at twilight as from the lion who devoured the lamb. Is it possible that we have been oversold on our essential evil—namely that underneath we are a caldron of bestial, murderous, incestuous urges. Perhaps we are not vicious brutes behind a thin veneer of civilized restraint. Can it be that we are not intrinsically worse than the great majority of creatures and that our destructiveness, hate and cruelty are not embedded in our chromosomes but are responses learned from living?

Although pleasant, perceptually gratifying, emotionally exhilarating LSD experiences are more frequent, unhappy, agonizing ones may also have to be lived through. The following passage from a nurse who has marked emotional problems indicates that when she begins to notice that her defenses are crumbling, she becomes terror-stricken.

I had an excited feeling in the pit of my stomach which usually accompanies the knowledge that "something is going to happen." I thought that the "happening" was going to be pleasant. However, soon I had the feeling of being choked from inside. I had difficulty breathing. Then I began to feel nauseated and restless. I said to the psychologist, "I don't feel good at all." Suddenly the tightness in my throat increased and I began to feel as if my body were on fire both inside and outside. My neck and back felt very tense. I became very frightened and had the feeling of acute panic. I was being swirled and sucked down, down, down, into oblivion. I clung to the table for dear life but it did no good. I fearfully cried out, "How long will this last? Will this go on all the time? I don't like this. I want out!" The fear was overwhelming me as I was thrust down into blackness. My body was burning up and I began to sweat. . . .

The indescribable feeling of being swirled and thrust into some place else was easing somewhat. It seemed that I had been in this torment for weeks. After it had eased up, I knew beyond a doubt that I was in another world. I felt it was no use telling the psychologist about it because he wouldn't understand. I remember thinking, "This is what the psychotic feels like." That feeling of panic and terror had left me tremulous and weak. My clothes and body were saturated with perspiration. I crawled up on the bed to rest. . . .

I sat at a table which was very uncomfortable. This made me more angry. I was already angry at having been subjected to such a painful and terrifying experience earlier. I was handed a piece of paper and a dull pencil. The worn-down pencil infuriated me and I threw it down and demanded another. The other was just as dull and I thought to myself, "Why doesn't the god-damned son-of-a-bitch go out and sharpen these pencils." . . .

The next test, I think, was drawing a figure. I drew one, but was angry and defiant. I didn't want to draw or even take any more tests. When asked to draw a figure of the opposite sex, I defiantly said, "There is no other sex" and refused to draw another figure.

Next came the vocabulary test. Once I got started

on it, I was fascinated to find that the words which were supposed to match were not really the right ones. I felt pleased and quite smug that I knew the correct definitions to the words, and that all the other people in the world were using the dictionary definition which was often entirely wrong.

Her aggressive impulses, ordinarily kept under good control, had been detected on the psychological tests preceding administration of the drug. When LSD reduced her ability to cope with the underlying drives, she became intensely anxious and hostile.

A philosophy student had a rather exceptional day. He was relaxed, tranquil, and described interesting changes in perception. His usual self-concern and critical self-appraisal were lessened.

The first noticeable external effect I saw was a remarkable brilliance and three-dimensionality in a photograph of a waterfall near autumn trees which was opposite me on the wall. The picture appeared to have a depth found in stereoscopic pictures, and the oranges and yellows of the leaves were vibrant and luminous. Next I noticed, while watching the discs on the tape recorder spin, that the corner screw on the top of the tape recorder lid was rotating also. This gave me considerable pleasure, as did everything else that occurred later.

When I started the tests I had a great satisfaction in reassuring the psychologist that I didn't mind his tests at all, and throughout the day I had a feeling of perfect confidence. However, my hand was trembling considerably, which interested but didn't seem to distress me. I was struck several times with the cleverness of the designer of the test. My efforts at reproduction were large, childish scrawls, but I felt no self-consciousness at my lack of dexterity, but a firm satisfaction at my productions. This feeling of benevolence toward myself and the experimenters was never strained throughout. I was asked to draw a person, a whole person, and I began with a large childish portrait of the psychologist. Next he asked me to draw a picture of a person of the opposite sex, and again I was struck with the cleverness of these tests. "You see," I thought, "this is a stock phrase—no matter what a person draws the first time, they ask for a person of the opposite sex next, and it always works out." Through this time I was experiencing a remarkable sense of peace, or of freedom from tensions, primarily tensions connected with self-consciousness. The normal inhibitions, the usual slight embarrassment, the usual critical reflection upon one's conduct or conversation were lacking.

Once he gave me a test consisting of incomplete series of words or numbers that the testee is to complete. I had difficulty perceiving what the logic of the series was even in the example given, but with some effort I managed to solve a few of the simplest ones, always happily surprised and pleased at having done so. As the test progressed and the problems became too hard, I was not disturbed. After some reflection I announced that this test consisted of some real puzzles, which I now had solved, and some projective material for which there wasn't any solution at all, but rather an opportunity to think of whatever one wanted. With this happy insight I finished off the rest of the test rapidly and at random.

Several times during the experiment I was asked to check on a long list of adjectives, those which expressed how I felt. It was with great joy that I progressed through boring, brooding, busy, etc., pleased when I found a word that applied, but not displeased with the many others that seemed sonorous, almost the loveliest poetry, but not really applicable. I had an ambivalence toward some words and considered them judiciously for some time without any emotional discomfort, and was uniformly pleased when having checked or not checked, I passed on.

On the Rorschach I had great pleasure over the shadings on the plain black-and-white cards. The cards aroused my boundless admiration and I repeatedly said that I hadn't appreciated what a fine and intricate set of patterns they were. I was impressed with the effect of overprinting, where one pattern was placed on top of another one. As I associated to the cards, it was much the atmosphere of a dream. I was floating along with the reverie, not watching it from the shore. At intervals the door opening or a glance at myself would remind me that I was in an experiment, that I had had a drug, that this was a strange experience, but this was not disturbing, just on a par with the rest of my reverie. The colored cards were magnificent. Each color seemed to carry its own feeling tone, all positive. The oranges,

reds and yellows were vital and expansive and sexual.
The blues and greens were cool, serene and rational. I
realized that normally I was a thinker more than a
feeler and I reveled in the warmer shades which
represented a release from obligation. But I didn't dis-
like the cool tones although I was aware that I couldn't
think much now. It secmed to me that probably the
rational activities were the better part, but the sensuous qualities of color and tension and activity were
attractive and engrossing now. I reflected several times
that I was giving much the same interpretations I had
some years earlier, the same volcanoes, the same sexual
symbols—only they were franker this time, the same
restless and powerful animals, but I wasn't a bit unhappy about this. Rather I admired the intensity of
images, the aliveness of the figures, without concern
about the interpretation the psychologist would put
upon these responses. There was no lack of images, I
could have gone on for a long time with the cards,
particularly the colored ones, which gave me great
pleasure, but I was vaguely aware of the test, and
proceeded more or less without prodding from card to
card.

Some time after the Rorschach, it was suggested we
go for lunch. The hall seemed lovely and impressive
and I remember remarking that it was quite a contrast
to the drab hall I had seen on entering; then it occurred
to me that this might not be a polite way to refer to
their building. But I felt they wouldn't mind, after all it
wasn't their responsibility the way the place was
decorated. My face was quite flushed and I looked

tousled and it must have been apparent to many that I was a patient or a subject. When I noticed an attendant or nurse looking at me curiously, I would momentarily think "I must look very odd." Normally I would be quite embarrassed at such attention, but I didn't mind it at all. Rather, I felt a warm affection for anyone interested in looking at me curiously. The canteen appeared as a beautiful and most attractive hall peopled by the loveliest of characters and filled with the most dazzling food. The salads, the meat balls, the vegetables, all were gloriously radiant. I did not feel hunger, nor a particular desire to eat any of this beautiful food, but I took a piece of apple pie and a cup of coffee and followed them out of this beautiful pillared hall into a courtyard which contained brightly painted red and green chairs. The colors seemed bright and beautiful, but I could remember that colors often seem this bright to me yet do not possess this mysterious loveliness and radiance. I commented that it seemed to be an alteration in the value of significance of the colors rather than the intensity of the color itself. We sat at a small table, slowly eating. The coffee was delicious, the pie thrilled me, but more the thought of the pie than the taste of it. . . .

———

After reflecting for a few days about the experience, he wrote the following.

The most impressive characteristic of the experience was an enormous and, for me, unique sense of freedom. Normally I am unconscious of the tension and strain under which I live, but the difference between my usual state and the one I enjoyed during this experience is so great that it could be compared to the lifting of a heavy burden. I don't know of any image which adequately suggests the difference between this state and my usual one; the best suggestion I can make is that the distance between the two states is as great as that between extreme mental anguish and my normal consciousness.

There was a profound change in my attitude toward myself. I had formerly believed that there were two of me: the surface person which was like the actor's role save that it was habitual and constant, and a deeper, more secret, powerful and somewhat malignant real self, which I kept concealed both from the world and from my surface self. The world was more or less successfully fooled into believing that the surface self was the real one, but I was aware that it was a sham and the real self was far less presentable, in fact, a sinister character. During the LSD experience this attitude was reversed. I strongly believed that the second, secret self was nonexistent. I was, in fact, just that fairly amiable, anxious to please and to be pleased surface self. I was just what I had thought I was pretending to be. Further, this self was clearly a product of my experience and volitions, there was nothing eternal nor even very enduring about it. It was a satisfactory self, a useful one, but neither particularly well disciplined or particularly intelligent, two things which mattered not at all. . . .

The second most impressive characteristic of the experience was a heightening of esthetic appreciation. Never have colors had the glowing, fascinating, delighting intensity that they had for me at the time. Faces, pictures, the hospital corridors and canteen, dishes, furniture, all seemed indescribably lovely and significant to me. I wondered at the time if the colors were actually more intense or whether the source of this loveliness was an increased significance attaching to them and an increased attention to them: I favored this latter explanation.

The entire experience seemed to be charged with value and significance; the world and its occupants seemed enormously beautiful, delightful and harmonious and I was included within that general harmony. Physically the experience was not restful; when the drug was at its greatest effect I was trembling, and when the effect was wearing off I was weary and restless. Emotionally and esthetically and religiously the experience was the most intense, impressive and valuable day I have ever experienced.

————

How is it that, if people achieve such a state of serenity and rapture, these drugs are not addicting? Can those who speak of "the most meaningful day of their lives" be content not to habitually seek out this sublime experience?

We offered another dose of LSD to the subject who had the most blissful response of all, in order to determine whether his reaction would again follow the same pattern.

After considering for a moment he said, "I don't think that I will take the drug again, at least not now."

"Why not?"

"I've had one wonderful day. Maybe we shouldn't ask for more than one such day in a lifetime."

The problem of addiction is discussed in detail in another chapter. At this point it should be said that true addiction does not occur, but habituation is a possibility.

The philosophy student's experience epitomizes the "good" reactions. He was uncritical, unconcerned, euphoric and impressed with the perceptual richness. "It was a real holiday," he said later.

The highlights of a psychologist's story illustrate a point. Her day was a varied one emotionally, ranging from depression to mystical feelings of unity. A knock on the door could change her mood markedly. Under LSD a person is vulnerable to such relatively minor incidents. Even minimal variations in the attitude of those with whom one is in contact may be sensed and may cause an intense response.

———

I could feel my tongue getting thick, and I couldn't answer questions quite properly. It felt as though the messages were all coming into the switchboard, and messages were going out all right, but that the switchboard was all jammed up and the two weren't coordinating. As though the operator had something else on her mind, or too much to do, and was just letting things get all jammed up. . . .

Then I suddenly saw the color of the wall waxing and waning—ebbing and flowing. The extraordinary character of light and color is unbelievable. There was a third dimensionality to color—and a constant change. And there would be a symphony of variations on what ordinarily is a plain brown wall. Or the flat yellow paint above it would suddenly light up the room and vary from pale translucent yellow to daffodil bright. The color would ebb from left to right, and then it would move from the floor up to the ceiling and back— always I was aware of the objects and the room, and although the things moved toward and away from me as though on waves, still they were actually fixed and I knew they were real. This was interesting—how dimension and color and other things all were mixed up in that they were all part of the whole pulsating ebb and flow, and it took enormous effort to try and separate things out sufficiently to describe what was happening accurately.

Just before the colors hit and just after the curtain started coming down between sections of my brain, I had that wonderful relaxation of the barriers which I have known before—the wonderful relief, the laying down of psychological burdens which has come to be identified in my thinking with the relaxation of the ego. I could feel myself being drawn into a mystical experience—the sense of unity with all things in the universe. I tried to describe this, and someone talked in terms of "sacred," which somehow wasn't right. Se-

mantically that had connotations of organized religion
and the dichotomy of sacred-profane which has no part
of this. It came to me just as it has in the past, with
profound humility and tears. This was quite a shift
from the silly predrunk feeling of giggliness I had had.
But as I felt the relaxing of the self boundaries, there was
this flood of grateful tears which I stopped because of
the three men present. . . .

It was the word-association test, and I was completely set to cooperate and to give associations. But
with the first word I realized that it was impossible.
There was no association at all. It was as though the
word had been released into a great bubble of space
and time and hung suspended there. It had no relationship with anything. And since it was completely irrelevant, I couldn't even attempt to find a word to go
with it. It would be like trying to answer a question in
color with a bar of music. I tried to tell them what it was
like—it was as though I were in the middle of a wide
and wonderful pasture—free and green and full of sun-
light, and something was going on back at the fence that
they wanted me to do. I was in the pasture, but the word
association test is part and parcel of the fence—which is
only an artificial barrier with no real intrinsic meaning
to the freedom of the pasture. It was trivial, and so
vastly irrelevant. It was almost impossible to see how
intelligent people could expect to find meaning to life
(which was the pasture) in contemplating designs of
the fence. . . .

He switched to the Shipley-Hartford, and I was able,
with great effort, to cope with the vocabulary test. It also

was extraordinarily irrelevant and silly. But I did it because he wanted me to. And then when it came to the second half, I really went through what a psychotic must go through. I couldn't concentrate; I couldn't think. In the first place I found the task meaningless and irrelevant. Secondly, the words would come up from the paper toward me and then recede—sometimes into one another and I couldn't read. And then when I looked at the word "red" I saw the color glowing from the page. I found that the words ran into one another and changed shapes. When I tried to write answers I couldn't coordinate, it was with great difficulty as though someone else were writing it. I kept thinking what a terrible thing we psychologists did to testees—here I who knew the test was having so terribly much trouble. And I thought, thank God, at least I know the test and thus manage a little. Which I think is important insight into motivational factors making up a psychologist.

I finally finished with great effort, and then the Draw-A-Person came. And I had a terrible struggle doing it—I just couldn't seem to do what was appropriate. I drew an old-fashioned little girl—and at the same time I really didn't want to—knowing that I was drawing myself. And I came up with a little girl where the head didn't belong with the body. The legs were all grown up but the head was a vapid child's head. And the dress was of the Victorian era.

The second figure was the really traumatic one, though, because I wanted to draw Little Lord Fauntleroy. Knowing that it was my masculine concept, I didn't want to put it down. But my honesty made me do

it, although my defensiveness changed it into a courtier
at the time of one of the Louis. That way it was more
acceptable. But I must say that insight into the man I
wanted to draw was devastating, and I felt it as such.

While I was feeling it—and also the ebb and flow and
change of colors—there was a sharp knock on the door,
and I was snapped back to "reality" as though I had
been plunged into a bucket of cold water. I felt as
though a knife had cut through things—and my psychological interpretation was of a sudden perception of
myself in a barren hotel room (I even said "hotel"
instead of "hospital"). I had an overwhelming sense of
depression—of the terrible barrenness and one-dimen-
sionality (because suddenly everything was flat and
colorless and cold and hard). I felt an overwhelming
sorrow for the transients who go from barren room to
barren room in life—so busy that they don't see anything or feel it in the going. Rooms flat—with no
relationship—no warmth—no life. And suddenly I saw
the difficulty. Life is the warmth and the flowing and
the three-dimensionality—but it becomes overwhelming to man who must compress into one dimension and
flatness and barrenness in order to deal with it. And
this necessity to deal with it comes when he tries to go
somewhere. It is the motion of trying to go—trying to
get some place is the difficulty—it is the cause of the
descent from Eden—the eviction from the pasture.
Because the minute that one tries to go someplace or get
somewhere, then one is not content to let things be—to
live and experience life. In order to "go" one must compress and flatten; the very directionality does that. In

our ardor to "be" something, we lose life, real life—and must content ourselves with this poor, flat, tawdry imitation. And we become so used to it that it seems to be real to us; the illusion has become the reality. And then we hurry faster to achieve and to "find" what we have lost. And the faster we go the flatter the dimensions become, the harder the corners, and the sharper the knives—until there are only the barren hotel rooms like cardboard sets on a stage with only actors going through them in a frenzied hurry—pushed by the restless anxiety to find meaning to life—when the very nature of their pressure and compulsion is what makes life unreal.

After the Draw-A-Person came the Bender-Gestalt, and I had fun with that. I had a lot of fun using paper on it. There was a feeling of expansiveness and a general flouting of authority. While I was doing it I knew that I ordinarily would put all the forms on one piece of paper. I'm so controlled and frugal. Anyway, I had no trouble with the Bender. I drew good figures and associated to them, and the great fun was putting them about three to a page. And I even craftily arranged it so that I had a whole sheet of paper for the last figure. It was like satisfying a compulsion to stuff one's mouth with food when you know it isn't polite. But such pleasure to take a whole sheet of paper for that last figure (and I even ran off at one end) .

I fought the sentence completion violently. It was so much effort. Why did I have to do it? It was like taking all the time and trouble to go out of the pasture through the gate, find out something trivial and then come all

the way back in to write it down. It was like being in
Germany and going over to France to find something
out in French and then coming back into Germany and
translating it into German so that I could record it.
And all of it very inconsequential and meaningless.
But the psychologist said I had to do it, it was important,
and he made me feel that I was being defensive, and my
desire to cooperate in the test won out over my lethargy
and feeling of irrelevance, and in order to do the task at
all I did it as fast as I could without thinking because if
I had thought I never could have done it—too much
effort, and I suppose defensiveness. And I knew as I was
writing that I was betraying myself—I felt unloved—
no one had loved me, etc.

———

These narrations extend across the entire scale of the
emotions, from utter panic to utter peace. Even while
being harassed with batteries of psychological tests, it
was possible for some subjects to be entranced with new
appearance of the commonplace. Some seemed to learn a
bit about themselves. Some had a rough day, some a
holiday.

8 *"All Is As New"*

In the preceding chapter the participants were held to rigid experimental procedure. In this chapter a variety of environments and purposes were imposed upon the subject. Some were patients in a study of the drug's therapeutic potential while others were gifted individuals whose creative capacities were being considered. As a rule the situation was less fixed and the invigilators more sympathetic and accepting.

The first two narrations are from people whose expressed purpose for taking LSD was self-understanding. They wanted a look at what seemed unreasonable, inexplicable and incomprehensible in their lives. They were lost; the maze of the past ended in a limbo of the present. These were no happy, but tormenting, suffering experiences. The uprooting of the jerry-built, overburdened postures of a lifetime was a fearsome, agonizing event. Not everyone could have endured the guilt-ridden memories that poured over the floodgates,

drenching the sufferers with sweat and tears. Not everyone is able to pass through to the other side of anguish.

This woman, obviously sophisticated in psychody-
namic constructs, was joined in a struggle with her past.
The bare roots of her childhood were seen all too clearly
and painfully. At one point she was overwhelmed and a
transient mental turmoil of psychotic proportions developed, but she was helped through to gain a belated
amity with herself.

Actually, I sort of expected a repetition of the freedom from self of the first session. But in reality I lived
through a massive reduction of my defenses and habit
patterns back to the very beginning of family identifications. All of these appeared in brilliant color, so,
although I was conscious of what was going on, I might
be said to have been hallucinating. I could stop the
process when I wanted to, but I tried to ride the
emotional and symbolic wave down to the bottom to
understand the whole story.

Almost the whole process was acute agony—pure
hell or purgation—and I realized it as such and spoke of
it thus. It was a purgation of the spirit through self-
knowledge; not just insightful knowledge, but also
emotional knowledge of a direct and actual and acute
sort. Almost the whole time I realized that I was enclosed in a wall of the defenses: I could see and feel
their limitation. But several times the light broke
through, and at the end when I was beaten and spent I

began the ascent to the light of wholeness and integration. . . .

Although the drug had been working for some time,
I remember having the feeling of waiting, waiting—
waiting for I knew not what. Then I saw spots of
brilliant color in small flecks or squares—the pure color
made when a prism diverts pure light. The flecks
danced all over to the music, and everything in between
was gray. To the left was a sly fox with a bushy tail. I
realized with anguish—because it became painful at the
very beginning—that analysis is my first line of defense:
I take reality and break it up into pieces because I cannot deal with it whole and pure. This makes flecks of
extraordinarily brilliant color, but the whole interplane
is gray. And how foxy I think the defense of analysis is!

Then I saw a white church and spire against a mauve
background, and this reminded me of a cardboard cover
for a record. Again a defense against the pure music
itself. I fought throughout the session to understand
and associate to these symbols. The little white church
with the high steeple at times had a woman standing beside it. She was all bundled up in warm clothes—mauve
with white trim—and it was cold. The woman became
in turn a madonna, a snow maiden, a snow man and
a gingerbread man. She and the church would alternate
and when the church was there, the shape of the gingerbread man stood beside it. Sometimes the church would
show just its bare bones—the ribbing like the prow of a
ship, and then the woman became the figurehead. And
at times the bare bones of the church changed into a

magnificent cathedral with the shadow of the structure still upon it. And I realized that these were the planes of the prism which contaminated the pure soaringness of the church—the bones of my defensive system.

As I experienced these symbols I relived the myth of Nordic supremacy—to my horror. I was made to feel the coldness, the austereness, the separateness of the myth that Nordic people are superior to others. I realized that this had been built into me from earliest childhood. I felt its austerity and its coldness—anyone who must be superior pays the price of snow and ice. And through these symbols I released the racial intolerance back and down to my childhood where I was brought up in the South—and I loosened part of my own need for feeling superior. The first line of defense: analysis. The second line of defense: prejudice and intolerance.

At one point I was Medusa, and then suddenly it was a permanent-wave machine, and finally it became the heavy headpiece of a diver's suit and I was under the ocean with this monstrously heavy equipment which seemed to be necessary for survival but merely kept me from being free and unencumbered in the lovely green water. And I felt anguish of this well-defendedness—of the desire to turn men to stone, of attempting to be beautiful, of protecting myself at the cost of others. And I felt the torment of this well-defendedness and this inability to be part of the ebb and flow of the unconscious world.

From this came the consideration of my relationship with men and of the basic problem of masculinity-femininity. In understanding the symbols I found that the madonna and the gingerbread man were two halves of myself which I could not get together into a whole—they were stereotypes of my misperceptions of the masculine and feminine parts of my nature. We followed this down—down through my relationships with sensitive men whom I had manipulated so that at times I felt I had driven them to the brink of death or insanity. I felt this in a violent way because the guilt and the misery of manipulation of the vulnerable was so overwhelming for me to face. I felt that I should be my brother's keeper, but instead I had used my brother for my own advantage. And I saw this with terrible and excruciating clarity in terms of how I had sided against my brother to win approval from my mother and father; I who knew how he felt and should have protected him! And how this relationship of fundamental competitiveness had become displaced with the years onto my relationship with men.

As the guilt piled up, I felt that I killed my father, turned my mother toward insanity and made my brother neurotic and latently homosexual. And it was too much. I went off into a tangential world and knew that I was insane. I could feel the enclosedness of it, the separateness, and worst of all—the symbolization. I saw giant mosquitoes which drilled into my skull and sucked out the brains. They were not alive but were mechanical —huge, impersonal, glittering insects with the flecks of brilliant color that were the sign of my analytic tendencies as decorations on their transparent, beautiful but completely unalive wings. And they swarmed around in complete silence. I told the therapists that they would have to pull me through—or I didn't know what would happen.

And we went back into the problem—I went down back into the past of the family identifications and re lived the necessity I was taught of the changing roles: how I had to shift identifications depending on the needs of those around me. And how I could never settle into either one of the two separate masculine-feminine halves. And suddenly I was the judge, and my two friends were pleading for my life and sanity. They tried to show me extenuating circumstances: I am the way I am because life had so shaped me. It wasn't enough. I said that I should have known better; that I must assume the full responsibility for what I was.

And then I heard one of them talking about the little girl who had not known which way to go; the little girl who had done the best she could and who had assumed the guilt of others; the little girl who was loved only for what she produced or accomplished and never for herself. And suddenly I had the absolute desperation of feeling that I was totally unloved. And it was all because I was too terrible a person; I was so horrible that I couldn't be loved.

"But it isn't your fault," they said.

"Yes, yes," I said. "It is my fault. It is, it is. I must accept the responsibility."

"How is it yours?" one asked.

"Because I am so unlovable," I answered. "That is my fault!"

"But that doesn't follow," they cried out in unison.

I looked up at them—startled. There was a silence.

The quiet voice started speaking. "Some people are just not capable of love. It's not that you were unlovable; it's just that *they* were incapable of loving you."

Suddenly the insight flooded my mind. It seemed like the truth. I burst into tears. It was over, and the untruth was finished and broken. I could feel the lifting of the weight and the magnificence of relief. And the light began welling up from the inside and outside.

———

This is the beginning and not the end of the struggle. But it is a hopeful beginning in the reconstruction of a life.

A housewife had many important situational problems which seemed insoluble. There was an impending divorce, financial difficulties and her own acting-out behavior. In the course of a few LSD sessions she became aware that her own inadequacies and insecurity had provoked the crisis. The problem was not "out there" but "in here."

. . . I was feeling very comfortable and relaxed when suddenly it happened. I started to cry uncontrollably and nothing could have stopped it—it was like a dam giving way. At first I didn't know what the weeping was about, but soon I became aware that I was reliving childhood experiences of which I had scarcely any conscious knowledge. Until today I had remembered only isolated fragments, but now the entire sequence reeled off as from a microfilm that surely was stored within my head. This reliving was very painful, and I could see that in burying it my life had been altered. One of the fabulous aspects of this microfilm was the clarity of color and form, from the facial expressions to the most minute details of the background. . . .

There was one sequence which appeared on my private stage that I was unwilling to face (out loud, I said it was inconsequential). This rejected material kept at me to the point that I had to let it come out. It was very unpleasant and I felt ashamed, guilty and just about the lowest piece of humanity. It was something that had to do with my relationship with my mother, something of which I had been unaware, yet I could see that it had caused a serious disturbance in my life. . . .

Finally, I gathered up enough courage to start working on this particular matter. It came out as a Hieronymus Bosch and gargoyles and Käthe Kollwitz, and it was unpleasant and frightening. With the help of the doctor I was able to complete this part of my personal torment and the stage brightened up immediately. . . .

But confusion and fright took over again. None of the pictures seemed to make sense. I felt literally out of my mind. The room and furniture were distorted, strange and terrifying. I was panic-stricken. I said to myself, "If I ever get out of here alive, I will never fool with this again. Anything is better than this." I struggled in mental agony, not knowing what the struggle was for. I had failed. The terror persisted and I didn't know what to do.

The doctor said, "Go into the terror. Force yourself into the worst of it."

I did. It was horrible, no, I was the horror. The horror was me.

Then peace came pouring over—flooding my mind and permeating my body. I knew that I never could be completely lonely again. I was not miserably apart, but a part of life.

The shameful memories have been burned to ashes, I think. It is impossible to express the humility I feel having had this terrible, wonderful glimpse of me.

A writer who has taken LSD and mescaline a number of times in an effort to examine the phenomena of altered consciousness and integral thought has drafted this overview of his experiences.

On the first occasion I had a preliminary disappointment. Havelock Ellis, Weir Mitchell, Aldous Huxley and many others said that color and design would be greatly heightened. This part of the experience, though it has never been wholly absent, has never proved outstanding. What succeeds it, the sense of the aliveness of everything, has, however, always been distinctive and fascinating. After the first awareness of tactile strangeness (a faintly unpleasant feeling as though the skin of the hands was thickened) there comes a dilation of the sensory frontiers (e.g., one feels as though one were part of the chair and the floor). There is no lightness or dizziness, but on the contrary a strong sensation of massivity, as though one were part of an immensely powerful living structure. The oncoming of the entire reaction is slow. Almost an hour for the first symptoms and a second hour before reaching that region which is generally the high tableland of the experience. In the two hours of the high experience there is first a unique intensification of awareness of human beings. If taken in full daylight, the human face seems to be a vortex of energy rather like a flower-shaped flame. Peculiarity of features by which we recognize individuals is not noticed. It seems at this point as though from the intensity of this flame-like structure one could diagnose temperament with considerable insight. If alone and in the dark, then the hypnagogic images are first crystal patterns colored and streaming up from lower left to upper right and next organic patterns (e.g., leaf and wing forms). These latter forms tend to reverse their direction—going horizontally from right to left. The forms are at first dense, becoming increasingly translucent and finally become lines of light moving at increasing speed—a shimmer of radiation. This conveys an intense sense of vitality. As the stream accelerates it grows clearer—as when, after diving, one swims up rapidly and sees the water breaking open above one into air and light. The light intensifies—generally topaz. The awareness of living interpenetrating light becomes a delight, as peaceful as it is fascinating. At this level the sense of personality is not so much lost or merged as vastly dilated till its frontiers are lost in a consciousness which is not that of an ego. If the ego is thought about, it is with the responsible detachment of a conscientious trustee; and painful events or anxious prospects are regarded with an interest free of any alarm; while actual pain is experienced without

distress or concern. Personal problems and universal rid-
dles such as the problem of evil can be considered with a
comprehensive acceptance that is neither resigned nor
indifferent. There are fluctuations at this level. The intensified enlargement of consciousness goes in waves;
troughs when one looks down and considers issues, crests
looking up toward sources. There is no euphoria. Indif-
ference is the feeling tone toward the body. The state of
mind is a delighted calm of complete significance, what
in Greek is called "eudaemonism."

Can anything more be said about this condition to
convey its quality? Probably not. But possibly something
might be remarked in regard to a state which sometimes
intervenes at this time of detachment. There is a key
phrase in the writings of the philosopher Nicholas of
Cusa. He speaks of a state of intense consciousness that
is possible, and only possible because the experience
goes "beyond the conflict of the opposites." The distinction between "I" and "it" and the division into "this and
that" have ceased. Dimension and quantity have gone.
Comparison and analysis cease. Polarity and orientation
are absent. This, though, is no sense of fogged awareness
or confused apprehension. Far from any sense of loss,
bewilderment or dimming, there is the most vivid recognition of a wholeness that is absolute, timeless, instant.
The comprehension is entire. If there is a feeling tone it
is one for which fathomless peace is too passive a word
and inexhaustible energy too febrile. This state is basic
and omnipenetrating. One does not "appreciate" it.
Every object and every self are aspects, scintillae and
constructs made by the separate consciousness in their

effort to objectivize and manipulate that timeless continuum. The experience is attended by a feeling for which "happiness" is the dimmest of approximations. Yet even to call it "feeling" is a misdescription. Coming down from it, joy is felt, and unstinted loving-kindness. But in itself it would seem to be nearer to a knowledge that is at last pure Truth—a Truth which is Reality and therefore transcending feeling, as we know it, and action as we strive to manifest it.

After the two-hour tableland the awareness of place and time, position, character and physique begin to re-emerge. At this point there is sometimes some euphoria. It may be no more than the release from the immobility. For generally one remains seated in the same position for a number of hours without shifting. At this point, phrases (attempts to define the experience) begin to form in the mind. Appetite for food begins to return. It is, till then, wholly absent. One is simply unaware of food as an interest, as a nonsmoker is unaware of tobacco as a sensory interest. For another twelve hours there is distinct, if slight, physical awareness of the state. Later on, the state of mind can be recollected at will, especially when waking from sleep. This causes or provokes a capacity to integrate otherwise irrelevant or frustrating experiences. Thanatophobia has never been in evidence in this subject's reveries, but certainly since these encounters a cheerful curiosity as to "out of the body" possibilities is increased. Not by nature either cheerful or generous, the subject's attitudes of mind in these respects seem to have been lastingly improved to some

extent. There appears to be no haunting wish to repeat
the experience. Though no doubt one learns to handle
the experience with great purposiveness, nevertheless
the conviction seems to be that one should learn by reflection afterward how to integrate these insights into
active living. The strong impression also is left in the
mind that one should be able to learn how to induce if
not to command this state of mind by an act of conscious
awareness made by the will when confronted with the
issues of social livelihood. In other words, the experience—at least in this case—seems to show the consciousness how it could handle emotional predicaments. It is
as though one had overlooked certain controls in an instrument, and by the means of a flashlight one's attention had been drawn to where they are situated. It
should also, I feel, be noted that frequently afterward
there is a momentary "opening" ("flash" would be too
spastic a word) when for maybe a couple of seconds an
area one is looking at casually, and indeed unthinkingly,
suddenly takes on the intense vividness, composition and
significance of things seen while in the psychedelic condition. This "scene" is nearly always a small field of
vision—sometimes a patch of grass, a spray of twigs, even
a piece of newspaper in the street or remains of a meal
on a plate. Seldom is it some fine selection of forms—
such as trees or flower beds; generally it is not a human
being unless it be simply the form, not "the person."
Hardly ever is it a distant view broad enough to be
called landscape. It seems strange to this subject that as
esthetics are not his principal concern these involuntary

moments of significance which give so strong a sense of "entirety" should always be provoked by visual beauty, not even by music or by character in action.

———————

Nothing need be added to this woman's description of her journey.

I hoped for understanding of that elusive, persistent nostalgia and the need to communicate, but otherwise avoided having any too preconceived idea of what the drug would do. I wanted just to let it happen whatever it might be. I felt nothing for about 45 minutes. I lay quietly and listened to the music I had brought with me. There were a few moments when a slight nausea was felt, but it vanished. Then my vision commenced to change a little. A slight tremor in it, the appearance of the room became faintly mottled, the outline of objects less fixed. And slowly the music seemed to absorb all my consciousness. It is as though all previous hearing of music had been deafness. It seemed to me as though the music and I became one. You do not hear it—you are the music. It seems to play in you. I thought that perhaps this complete experiencing of it is the way a real musician perceives it all the time.

As the effect increased, the music seemed to take over the direction of the experience. I began to feel disembodied, and a marvelous weightlessness commenced. My consciousness seemed to rise into a wonderful limitless space, infinite and curving as the sky, with the earth and sea below. It reminded me of the hawks I have so often watched, soaring effortlessly on updrafts over the canyons and hills. The colors of the sky and sea and mountains were marvelously beautiful in a sort of shining air. There was only nature, no buildings anywhere. Only the land, the ocean and the limitless vaulted sky. It was absorbing and beautiful, beyond speech. I wanted not to speak, only to experience it silently. The music seemed to speak beyond any eloquence. Nothing in words could conceivably add to it. I had to force myself to try to speak even a little.

After a while the subject of the problem of communication in everyday life came back to mind and with it the sense of this need. This was very painful. Then I began to see what the music seemed to be telling me— that none of that dreadful human need was necessary. That it is because we do not perceive this other marvelous, limitless state that we become lost in a wilderness and flounder. Somehow, now, barriers and blinds drop the fencing of our perception, and another state of reality is realized. It occurred to me how strange it would be if some inkling of this state drives one mad. As if the mad person knows this state exists and not being in it drives him mad. I began to feel what the nostalgia might be. It is in the knowledge, somehow, of this state. The soaring extraordinary light and bliss. The reverent sense of clear reality. And the knowledge that nothing that is utterable is real because this indescribable state is so much greater. The nostalgia is toward this knowledge.

I saw only one other person, my husband. I saw us together climbing slowly up a winding mountain path. I

understood the experience in relation to him. And the
need to share the experience with him. And that the being in love is the truth of all this.

Throughout everything the music seemed an intrinsic
part of the experience. I couldn't then or now imagine
what it would have been like without it. Parts of the music were far more meaningful than others. The lighter,
more delicate parts of Mozart and Beethoven, particularly the piano parts seemed at times the very voice and
description of the ecstatic feeling. The deeper, more
fully orchestrated parts sometimes seemed too overwhelming and became literally noise. I was at all times
aware of surroundings, the hospital noises, etc., but they
were unimportant and I didn't think about them. The
tape recorder we used was distracting largely because of
my own sense of obligation to try to talk into it whenever it was on and the effort to talk at all was a burden. I
would have preferred to be silent and gone further into
the drug. It seemed to induce an effortless, absorbed and
timeless power of inward-turned concentration. One *is*
the thought. Again it occurred to me that this immense
concentration, so effortless and sustained, might be one
of the reaches of the mind in highly gifted people. That
they might be able to achieve this on their own in daily
life, and out of it comes creative thought.

The feeling of being disembodied continued throughout. At times my mind seemed to float above my body. It
could be anywhere spatially at any moment. The prevailing feeling was the marvelous soaring in the universe, the immense light and a being borne aloft by the
music. I felt without will. The music, the drug, and sub-

jective forces inside seemed to determine what happened. There was no particular sense of time. Also, most important—none of any of this seemed strange or new. It seemed more real than ordinary consciousness and all of it seemed "revisited." Something one had known once. It was as though there were a reality, which even with the help of the drug, one was catching merest glimpses of—perhaps like sun seen through forest trees. And certain factors in one's self and the opening of the drug enable one to see—however much or little according to the person and the moment. But what you see you know is not illusion.

Toward the end of the session when it was lessening I looked about in curiosity and it occurred to me that being dead might be like this. I also had the impulse to try to communicate with my husband who was elsewhere at the time. I was also aware of an odd religious, almost ritualistic, impulse to make an offering, a sacrifice, as though this gesture had some mystical meaning. There seemed a level of symbolism that one could stay in for a while, but it didn't seem too important. Then I saw, when the drug was fading, some demons . . . small dancing creatures. They came in flocks, like little shore birds moving very rapidly. They seemed entertaining, not alarming or particularly important. I asked myself what they might be and instantly knew. They were doubts. My critical thoughts of this experience.

I could have stayed in this half-state and explored it and it would have been interesting, but I could feel it was the fading of the other, and I also felt that I had learned what I was to learn. I was afraid to take more of other people's time and thought it was time I emerged from this. Perhaps coming out was too hurried, as later that night I had a severe headache, but none of that is important. I remain with a vivid awareness of the experience. At times music seems to start to evoke the drug. I have not tried this seriously yet, but will when time determines it. It was a profoundly moving, real and deeply meaningful experience.

———

The following report will be of interest to those studying the effects of the environment upon the nature of the LSD response. The subject was familiar with the drug. To determine the changes produced by sensory deprivation in combination with LSD, he was placed in a soundproofed, totally dark room for six hours. The experience was described as more intense than under ordinary conditions.

I took long swoops up and away from everything that makes me B. Away from his body with its appetites and its clamorings, away from his mind with its conceptualizing, its speculations and its constant pursuit of security, away from the world in which his body and mind operate and on which they make their demands. Yet I never felt the least bit of alarm—only a great exuberance and wonder. For between swoops I could return to B. and be completely reoriented in a second. I seemed to be always touching him lightly so that he was there for a point of reference, but I was not held by him. Although I lost all sense of "me-ness" the sense of "I-ness" was in-

tensified unbelievably. When I came back to B. (me-
ness) I could say "I am B." But when I swooped I could
only say "I" or "I am." It was simply a sense of "is-ness"
or "am-ness." I wasn't anything—I simply was. And at
these moments of really ecstatic clarity there was such
peace and rest and at the same time such exuberance
and wildest joy. It was something like the short respites
(only magnified a million times) which one gets when
everything in everyday life seems for a moment or two
to make sense, when suddenly there are no problems to
struggle with or find answers to.

At least three times I dropped back down to B.,
quickly reoriented myself, took stock of what was happening and then "took off" again. And each of these
times I came down I found that I was desperately trying
to translate some of this experience into words or
phrases that I could hang on to and that would act as
some kind of symbol through which I could recall the
experience.

I can only remember some of these phrases—"Do I
really know what is going on 'out there' (in the everyday
world) because I see it or because I am willing it?"—
"Don't, don't, don't usurp the is-ness of is or the be-ness
of being!"—"The Universe is happening itself."

At one of these "landings" it came to me very force-
fully (and as though I were recognizing something that
I had always known but had refused to look at) that the
real secret of understanding what this life is all about is
in tracing thoughts and ideas back to their source—not
following them outward in their implications and developments. Otherwise, we can only develop (or hope to

develop) an infinite capacity for knowledge of an infinite number of things. It seemed that in this sense of "I-ness" was the answer to "What is that out there?" For in some strange way the "I-ness" did not exist in relation to anything—everything existed in relation to it. It was the very source of all that out there. . . .

Finally, I knew that I was back to stay, that B. had now gotten hold of me again. For I suddenly remembered an old resentment against someone. I made some attempts to soar again but with no success. For the next two hours I remained in the dark and watched as B. slowly but surely took over. This is the part of the experience that is understandably horrifying to some people, I should think. But since I have spent too many years consciously struggling with B., I was bored rather than horrified.

I was still feeling the LSD when I had a rather interesting fantasy or daydream. The sort of thing that often happens if one sits quietly and indulges in a reverie. It was not an hallucination, it was not visibly "out there" although it was very vivid and I could "see" it inside. But the imagery was the same that accompanies any kind of thinking. I think of a person and I "see" their face. I was imagining this but not of my own will:

I was standing in the bow of a large boat. I had a great sense of catastrophe and danger, the water was rough and a wind was howling. I held a hawser in my hand and could cast off and get away to safety any moment I chose. There were crowds of people on the shore, all saying "Take me, take me." The first person I saw was G. I called him aboard and was about to cast off when I saw someone else I knew and called him aboard. Then someone else and someone else. Now people were turning up with whom I had had trouble in the past and against whom I had felt a great resentment. Each time one of these persons turned up, my resentments melted and I urged them to come aboard, knowing that I could never leave them. Soon I abandoned all pretense at control and stood back as the crowd rushed aboard. And then suddenly I realized that not only everyone but everything was aboard. We were all together and we were all safe. Everyone and everything was in the boat, the storm was in the boat, and the boat was in the boat, there was nothing else.

———

Excerpts from two reports by one woman demonstrate the variable nature of the LSD experience. The first time she dealt with external matters. The second encounter was directed inward, to examine and come to grips with some personal problems.

During the first experience she was in a harmonious, attractive setting in the company of friends with similar interests in art, philosophy, history and religion. Years of meditation had been appropriate preparation for this day.

About three-quarters of an hour after the beginning of the experiment a different quality of consciousness came with a rush. Nothing was definably changed, but the room was suddenly transfigured. All objects stood out in space in an amazing way and seemed luminous. I was aware of the space between objects, which was pure vibrating crystal. Everything was beautiful. Everything was right. Each smallest thing was uniquely important yet fitted perfectly into the whole. My little ego seemed removed, and I felt that I saw clearly and purely for the first time in my life. I wept with relief and joy. I felt unworthy of such blessedness. The tears streamed down like a releasing fountain. I felt no tension, no self-consciousness, no self-concern; only an all comprehensive well-being. I became aware of my body as slightly removed from me, massive yet well integrated, heavy yet light, my head freely floating on my neck. I got up from the chair and walked around slowly. I was surprised to find it so easy and rhythmic. I was delighted to find my feet just reached the floor and the floor came up softly to meet them.

As I looked around, the colors in the room became more vivid. The greens and blues were particularly lovely. Each object that I looked at held my fascinated attention. Each had a proper place in this crystal space. The living essence of each seemed ready to break through its clear-cut outline. I, too, had my unique place in this living space. I, too, was expressing some inner essence of being. I was relieved to feel that even I was contributing to the order and rightness that pervaded the room. I felt "enclosed in measureless content," poised, free.

I looked again at the beautiful space in the room and tried to decide why it was so satisfying. I said, "It is poignantly lovely, but I can't explain why. There is a divine ordinariness about it and yet it is completely differ-

ent. In some way it reconciles the opposites—heaviness
and lightness, movement and stillness, sound and silence, form and essence.

We walked around the garden together. It was like
walking in Paradise. Everything was composed and har-
monized. I felt I had never really seen this garden before. I was enchanted with each plant, leaf, flower, tree
trunk and the earth itself. Each blade of grass stood up
separate and distinct, edged with light. Each was supremely important. The subtle colors of the loose earth
and dead leaves were rich and wonderful. The vistas
through the shrubbery were magically intriguing.
Strangely enough I preferred the subtle colors to the
bright flowers. They seemed more mysteriously beautiful. I stood still and listened. I was aware of a profound
living silence, with all the sounds floating on top of it. I
looked at the faces of my friends again. Yes, people were
the most wonderful of all; beauty in faces and nature is
only the outer expression of love, love is the inner reality, love is the whole answer. Love is at the core and in-
forms all the forms. The crystal continuum is somehow
love itself shining through the varied shapes, expressing
itself most intensely in human beings. I was supremely
happy just standing and looking in any direction. The
beauty of the trees simply gave itself away. Creation was
good and it was an open secret.

We went into the house, and a record of the first Bach
Partita was playing. It was beautiful. The notes were
suspended in the crystal space like petals or leaves. They
wove themselves into garlands. I felt surrounded by the
music, not as if I were listening to it. And no matter how

far the sweeping strands of sound were flung out into space they always came around again to the same center, ending there with complete affirmation. . . .

———

A half year later, in the same setting, a similar amount of LSD was given with an entirely different result.

Before I took it this time I decided on an inner journey. There were certain things I wanted to face in myself and certain questions I wanted to ask. I wanted to be mostly by myself. . . .

I felt tightness in the solar plexus. I felt nervously restless and paced up and down the room. I felt no release from my ego, only more in its grip. I went to my room and tried to meditate but could not. I tried having a Bach record played. The music meant nothing to me but disconnected sounds. I felt miserable and discouraged, for I had counted greatly on this experience, as this was a critical time for me psychologically.

I asked that Handel's *Solomon* be played. As the music started, I suddenly felt a great lifting from within. Then outer space became alive. The music surrounded me with its great impersonal patterns. The music carried me and flowed through me. I felt in balance, harmony, freedom. All constriction fell away. I felt much larger than normal and more elongated in my limbs. The music gradually drew me down to the floor and curled me up into a compact ball with my forehead on the ground. I became a seed sown in a field of music. It poured over and around me. I was perfectly still, content to stay quiet and germinate. I knew I must wait there in the earth giving up everything. Parts of the music were songs and choruses, but the only words I heard were "How vain were all I knew" very clearly over and over. Yes, I realized I knew nothing and must be satisfied to *be* nothing but a potential. I felt I remained there lapped in music for centuries.

Finally I rose and moved slowly about the room, softly like a milkweed seed carried on air. I stopped before a crystal bowl of flowering quince that I had arranged the day before on a round glass-topped table. I saw it as a universal symbol—a mandala. Everything was there in microcosm with shoot, fruit and flower at the center. . . .

Whenever I shut my eyes I went through the most intense suffering I ever experienced. Everything disappeared and I was suspended over a black abyss and was being stretched as if between two worlds. I could hardly bear it, but I felt it necessary that I should endure. I kept my eyes shut as long as I could, for I knew something good would come of this—though what, I had no idea. I knew I could not put a time limit on the stretching. This seemed to go on for years. Then I began to *see* myself being stretched over the abyss, not only feel it. I saw my dark figure outlined with sparkling, shimmering lights. The suffering was just as intense, but I saw clearly that I must not resist but give in to it so that I could be stretched further. This stretching was somehow capacity for compassion. It was horizontal. I must endure it— endure compassion without being able to help.

Now, though still being stretched, I was detached

enough to ask some of my questions. Each was answered clearly by two words, "Let go." When it came to the question "Do I have any deep, unacknowledged fear?" the answer was, "Yes, you are afraid to let go." Then I asked, "What should be my relation to Ultimate Reality, to God?" "Endure not to know." That was the hardest to accept.

My friends came into my room. I was still sitting on my bed and still "like Niobe all tears." I tried to explain to them what I had been experiencing. I said, "I hope this weeping doesn't distress you. I'm being stretched but I'm accepting it of my own free will. I want to be stretched more and more until I let go, let go, let go. It's agonizing but it's not impossible to endure. My special difficulty now is not to *do* anything and now to *know* what is happening. I've always been the doer, the planner. I try too hard. But I can't now. Something important is being *done to me* and I don't know how long it will take. I just have to endure without struggling. I must wait for the completion to come in its own time. I'm on the woman's side of the universe—something I have neglected most of my life. Now I must allow it to overwhelm me, sink me to the bottom of the sea and stretch me. How young we all are in this life! How blindly blundering! How infinitely promising! I'm beginning to understand something very profound and very funny—I think you two had better leave me now. I'm talking too much. I should continue experiencing in silence. I have still more stretching to live through."

They both left the room. I closed my eyes and was taken back to an event that happened in San Francisco

two months ago. It didn't seem important at the time. I
was with two friends in the Art Museum seeing the
Robinson collection. Now I relived the sequence, only I
knew I had had LSD and was purposely returning. I
looked deep into the pictures three-dimensionally. As
before I went down to the basement alone before leaving—this time because I felt my friends could not understand what I was looking for. I looked at the same
grotesque pen-and-ink drawings by some contemporary
artist. Instead of paper they were etched on white light
as if they were drawn with thin black wires. One was a
distorted Christ figure crucified on the ground among
telephone wires—a modern rendering, I thought, of cru-
cifixion by means of broken communications. I understood what that meant. The other picture I looked at
was the "Three Marys at the Tomb", elongated, seem-
ing part of the rock entrance. I felt I must lie down
right there on the cold stone floor, stretched out full
length and let something in me die. But just then two
strangers (as before) came down the stairs. The basement faded and changed into the porpoise pool at Ma-
rineland, only much bigger.

I was on my back at the bottom of it nailed down and
still being stretched, still suffering intensely. Another,
more alive part of me, was a porpoise swimming freely
and joyfully up and down and around the pool. Sometimes I dove swiftly toward the bottom, then powerfully
shot up out of the water into the air. Whenever this happened it was an ecstatic experience. The air was pure
white light, limitless, dazzling, incomparably beautiful,
life-giving. The drops of water that fell from me as I

leaped were rainbow-colored sparks. I longed to stay up
—this was Reality, Life, Being—but I couldn't stay. I
plunged back again into the pool. I felt that on one of
my leaps into the Light I would give birth to a baby
porpoise! I kept returning to the Light as often as I
could. I thought, "This is the truth behind all religions.
Yet the outer expression of every religion is about as relevant to the Light as this Christmas tree at the bottom of
the Porpoise Pool." (They actually had one at Marine-
land over the holidays!)

By now there were three awarenesses in me—myself
nailed to the bottom, the free-swimming me, and an
observer. The latter felt rather sorry for her below,
but knew it was good for her to remain there longer.
Her suffering continued but did not disturb the other
two of us.

I tried to explain when my friends returned that I
was still nailed down and that I was glad of it. I said,
"The other time I had LSD I slipped past the ego and
had a wonderful time. Afterward I merged right back
into it. This time she is not getting off so easily. She has
been stretched unmercifully. I've told her not to struggle, as that only makes it harder for me. Worse than
that, it might lead to a negative, even a horrible experience. I see that as a possibility. But by willingly giving
way to the pain something real can be accomplished. I
may not remember exactly what it is—I have already
forgotten so much—but that doesn't matter. Something
is being done deep down."

Then a wave of intense suffering swept the three
awarenesses in me together. I said, "I feel that I shall

either die or give birth to a little porpoise. Or maybe both. That sounds ridiculous but it is true. Porpoises have to leap out of the sea to give birth to their young." Then I laughed and said, "I feel as if I were part Virgin Mary and part porpoise!"—meaning I had to bring forth something not of this world, something alive in spirit and in truth . . .

————

Much of a highly personal nature was not included in this summary. The subject felt that the suffering was a necessary part of the understanding which was attained during the hours of living through the problem. With the resolution of the conflict came a sense of harmony and wholeness.

She had decided to go on an "inward journey" during the second session, and this is the road she went. Sometimes the LSD experience may be willfully directed along predetermined lines. This is by no means invariable, often one is swept into unexpected, even unwanted tangents.

During the subject's first trial with LSD the external world was seen as strange and transfigured. Objects, even empty space were extraordinarily transformed and inspired awe and fascination. Psychiatrists speak of similar states as derealization.

In the second LSD experience she spoke of three separate awarenesses. The impression that the self has been transformed is called depersonalization. The strange sense of body alteration may be fragmentary; one extremity might seem larger or smaller. In this instance three coexisting identities in space, each containing some quality of me-ness, are described. Another subject wrote: "I saw myself as a mile-high Buddha. Looking down across my billowing belly to the road below, I could see another Me, the size of an ant. We looked at each other for a long time and each of us understood what the other Me meant." From another report: "I was sprawled on the sofa, arms and legs spread out and eyes closed. But I was also sitting on top of the bookcase watching the fellow on the sofa. He was going through Hell, and I felt a little sorry for him."

Portions of a report from a scientist exemplify a number of interesting aspects of the state.

One's expectations seem to have but little influence on the LSD reaction. Just before taking the drug I had received news of the suicide of a friend—my best friend. I decided to go ahead with the experiment despite the anticipation of suffering through this blow. There had been considerable identification with M., and his incomprehensible suicide had a shaking effect which left me groping for an answer. Furthermore, I was fully aware of many unresolved personal problems which might be nasty to face, although I had no objection to confronting them.

I don't know how soon after taking the drug I came to realize that it would be far from hellish. The feeling of happiness grew until, at its height, I thought I might burst from this overwhelming emotion. Joy overflowed the mind and invaded the body until it bubbled. "Protoplasmic joy—cellular gladness" were the words that came to me. My skin was bathed in tingling champagne and my fingertips discharged a pringling, vibrating current.

I deliberately thought of M.'s suicide, but the hyperphoria could not be diminished. M.'s death no longer appeared to be a waste—a bitter mistake. Somehow it fitted into the structure of life. . . .

Then there were the crosscurrents that flowed past— layer upon tilted layer. Even when I was convinced of the elemental goodness of life, there were secondary thoughts. Why should I feel this good? Would I remember? How did this stuff work? . . .

Personal insights were few. If the experience itself does not transmute, then all I had was a remarkable day. But it is difficult to believe that a marrow-shaking force of an intensity that leaves the body quaking does not leave its imprint somewhere. . . .

It was terribly hard to know when knowing reverberated down a hundred corridors. One thought, a hundred corridors, a thousand rooms, each with an existence of its own. I tried to order them and they swept on, leaving me with words . . .

Time. Each second separated by infinity. The Camera has stopped, and the world is caught in a silly snapshot pose. To see it so is enough to make one burst into laughter. . . .

There was a period of deep, surging, elemental movement. Upon emerging, one could speak only of the emergent levels, not of the depths. One felt muscle-weary, worn, as though pounded by high seas. This was a primal surge of unnamed energy without direction or structure, amazing in its power. It was impossible to identify or measure the flow. One could only align one-self in the streaming torrent or the turbulence became overwhelming. I was swept along relentlessly. To be one with the current was wisdom, for this was life itself rac-ing past. To oppose it was disaster. As the effects of the drug wore off, the torrent split up into hunger, survival and other recognizable drives and appetites. Now it was possible to observe it from firm ground. From here I could extrapolate back to that nameless deluge beyond cognition, beyond that pale thing we call emotion. . . .

I feel that this description is like an aerial view of an expedition into an abyss. One sees the trail leading in and the path coming out. The bottomless chasm remains invisible.

———

These are the unusual, uncanny stories of a diverse group of people, each having divergent experiences, each interpreting them after his own fashion. It is evident that what happens is apart from everyday aware-ness. The intensity of impressions, the extreme sim-plicity or complexity of consciousness, the sense of spatial and temporal discreteness and yet also of related-ness, the singular ego changes, all have been described. These changes occurring within a matrix of uncritical acceptance have a tremendous impact. Some reject them as illusory or psychotic, others accept them as having a meaning exceeding ordinary understanding.

It is unnecessary to pass final judgment upon these

states now. Their value to the individual may be open to question, but the importance of investigating the condition itself is obvious. These are unusual manifestations of human mental function, ordinarily inaccessible. The ability to produce them chemically clarifies similar obscure and puzzling experiences found in the religious, historical and mystical literature.

9 Psychotherapy with LSD: Pro and Con

One of the not always dispassionate dialogues about LSD concerns its place in psychotherapy. The very forceful opinions range from a complete denial that a drug of this sort could have any usefulness to the bald statement that it induces miraculous cures.

In order to make some sense out of the contradictory and confusing claims, it would be well to consider first what psychotherapy is and then what its goals are. These matters are neither simple nor generally agreed upon, and part of the confusion stems from the difficulty of definitions.

At the outset it can be asserted with a reasonable degree of confidence that psychotherapy is a learning process. It is the learning of new attitudes, new feelings and new behavior. This is a fair but overgeneralized description. The reason why most people seek psychotherapeutic help is because they finally realize that their present ways of living are distressing, ineffective or damaging. Their existing patterns of thinking, feeling and responding are the result of poor habits—maladaptive acquisitions of a lifetime.

Generally we learn in order to gratify some need or to avoid unpleasure. But our innate curiosity, the process of growth and cultural influences are also goads to the acquisition of new sequences of behavior. We seem to learn in two ways: by conditioning and by cognition. Some of our basic patterns are acquired by repetitive responses to stimuli associated with either a reward or punishment. If rewarded, the response is reinforced; if punished, it tends to be extinguished. Eventually, conditioning occurs, and the learned response becomes a part of our established psychological and physiological reaction pattern. Cognitive learning develops without conditioning and can result from single rather than from multiple events. The alternatives may be understood and the best response may be conceptualized rather than learned by trial and error. Cognitive learning can also be acquired by imitation; speech and other skills are mastered in this fashion.

The psychotherapeutic dilemma is how to get the patient to abandon the ingrained patterns for others which are more effective and mature. Neurotic patterns are especially resistant to extinction because, despite their discomfort, they seem to gratify some need of the patient. Such advocates of therapeutic conditioning as Skinner insist that retraining is a matter of repetition and reinforcement of proper stimuli which invokes the desired response until it becomes habitual. The

Freudians claim that new emotional and cognitive insights are necessary before change can occur. At one time the recovery of repressed childhood conflicts and the emotional abreaction to them was thought to be the crucial factor. Later the "working through" of the patient's resistances and of his disturbed key relationships became the central issue.

Insight can be understood as the sense made by the therapist and the patient out of the obscure patchwork of words which the patient expresses. Some of the material is his life story, some of the fabric are dreams, free associations and other fantasy material. The nature of the insight will vary according to the mold the psychotherapist uses to formulate the material. Judd Marmor believes that although the explanation given by different therapists will vary, each interpretation has a definite relationship to the life pattern of the patient. A Freudian may express it in terms of unresolved Oedipal complexes, a Jungian will speak of archetypes, a Rankian of separation anxiety, and a Sullivanian of oral dynamisms. Marmor's point is that they are all structuring the data in their own terminology, but that a common core of reality underlies each of the explanations.

The value of the therapist's formulations can be looked upon more nihilistically. Any explanation of the patient's problems, if firmly believed by both the therapist and the patient, constitutes insight or is as useful as insight. It is the faith, not the validity, that counts. It is curious how under LSD the fondest theories of the therapist are confirmed by his patient. Freudian symbols come out of the mouths of patients with Freudian analysts. Those who have Jungian therapists deal with the collective unconscious and with archetypal images. The patient senses the frame of reference to be employed, and his associations and dreams are molded to it. Therefore the validity of any school of healing should not be based upon productions of the patient— especially LSD patients.

Intellectual insight is not as highly thought of as emotional insight. The latter is accompanied by an abreaction, or discharge, of emotion after the validity of the insight has been accepted. During this period of emotional turbulence the patient is supposed to be more amenable to change. If the patient "discovers" the insight with only a subtle assist from the therapist, so much the better. It is easy to see how new knowledge about the onset of neurotic behavior will be a fine opportunity to begin to alter it. But insight alone is not ordinarily enough to do the job. A repetitious, some-times prolonged, relearning process must be instituted. Otherwise the patient backslides into the old habits.

Eventually the therapist becomes a highly significant figure to the patient. His notions of what is good and desirable tend to be adopted by the patient, and the therapist's overt or covert expressions of approval or disapproval come to constitute reward or punishment. Greater success in dealing with the immediate problems met with outside the therapist's office is another source of reward which keeps the patient learning the more adaptive responses. More important than any other single factor is the relationship that develops between the patient and his therapist. Relearning occurs best in an atmosphere of trust and faith. When the patient sees the therapist as understanding, considerate and devoted, he is willing to begin the hurtful process of changing.

From what has been said, it can be deduced that insight into the devious behavior or the conflict under- lying it may be unnecessary for therapeutic change to occur. It may be unnecessary, but it motivates the patient to work harder at his reconstruction. When someone has lived through decades of defective relation- ships and inconsistent communications with the impor- tant people in his life, this can be no simple or brief matter. Marmor states, "There is no substitute for the time-consuming process of patiently re-educating the patient concerning the nature of his perceptual, emo- tional, symbolic, and behavioral distortions, and ena- bling him by the working through process, to generalize and apply his increased understanding to many different life situations." [1]

A thoroughgoing personality reconstruction is the aim of some schools of therapy, such as the classical psychoanalysts. Others—the behaviorists, for example— are content with relief of symptoms. Analysts will claim that to relieve one symptom, such as hysterical blindness, will only lead to a substitute symptom; it is the buried conflict that must be resolved or its pressure will break out in new symptoms. The behaviorists reply that symptom substitution practically never occurs and that once the disability has been alleviated, further improve- ment in the emotional and perceptual distortions can accrue. The rapid removal of psychic symptoms, such as stuttering and enuresis, need not lead to the formation of new difficulties. If the loss of the symptom helps the patient adjust better, or if the need to retain the symptom is past, the substitution of other symptoms need not develop. One of the charges against LSD-type therapy is that it only relieves symptoms and does not alter the character structure. This is often true, but it need not be.

Since LSD therapy is often brief, it would be helpful to know whether rapid personality change can actually occur. When Pavlov's conditioned dogs were caged in a cellar that flooded one night, that single stressful exposure was so shaking that much of their conditioned learning was lost. In humans these stressful occurrences, during therapy or otherwise, have been called corrective emotional experiences. Behavioral and personality reshuffling has taken place following a momentous personal event. If it occurs at a time when the individual is psychologically ready to change, the personality realignment is dramatic and persisting.

It seems that intense and impressive psychic experiences make possible the sudden unlearning of ineffective ways of performing. After that, more satisfactory or more mature methods of functioning can be learned at an accelerated rate, perhaps even without outside help. This is far from invariable; most people will tend to slip back into the old, implanted habits. Rapid personality change is a possibility, but the hope for it exceeds its incidence.

If a question remains as to quick changes in ego structure, we know that rapid superego alterations are quite attainable. Some of the more malignant emotional disorders of which patients complain are due to the excessive punishments their rigid and overstrict consciences mete out. Over and above what might be called appropriate guilt and shame, many patients belabor themselves with massive self-condemnation, which often evolves into a serious depression. Unjustified feelings of failure, constant self-depreciation or inordinately high standards lead to much unnecessary suffering. Unreasonable fears—for example, the earlier myth that masturbation led to madness—have marred many lives unnecessarily. These are quite readily amenable to re-education, especially during periods of nervous system arousal, as during the LSD state. Their resolution can be sudden when the extraordinary experience allows the patient a new look at his old values.

The various goals of psychotherapy are pertinent background information to assay LSD's role in psychotherapy. Naturally these will vary widely from person to person, according to his needs and his capacity to change. The following list of desirable aims which are generally agreed to be in the direction of personality growth are not given in order of importance.

1. The relief of distressing psychic or psychosomatic symptoms.

2. A reduction of neurotic anxiety with a retention of "realistic anxiety."

3. Personal feelings of worth, meaning and hope.

4. Feelings of self-fulfillment in work or other activities.

5. The ability to express "healthy" aggression in an acceptable manner.

6. A high level of functioning commensurate with one's capabilities.

7. The capacity to know oneself without too much distortion. This requires that one's defensiveness not be excessive.

8. The capacity to enjoy the physiological pleasures.

9. Flexibility and adaptability to life stress; the capacity to endure, or, when necessary, to compromise.

10. Low levels of stereotypy in thought content.

11. An appropriate sense of responsibility.

12. A capacity to love and be loved.

13. A satisfactory relationship to authority; the acceptance of good or necessary authority; the willingness to struggle against bad authority realistically.

14. An ability to tolerate ambiguity and dissonance in the environment.

15. An awareness of the immediate and distant situation.

16. Sensitivity to the needs, feelings and thoughts of others.

17. The ability to see oneself and one's culture with a measure of humor.

Naturally all these desirable objectives are never completely achieved. We spend a lifetime, with or without professional assistance, moving toward and away from maturity. The difficulties of evaluating the goals of psychotherapy are evident. They are intangible, shift with cultural movements and can be measured only crudely with the devices now available.

Some comparisons between brainwashing and psychotherapy techniques may be instructive. There are interesting parallels which have implications for our interest in LSD therapy. Brainwashing can be defined as an effort to rapidly change thinking and behavior to conform to a specific political value system. Its practitioners believe that it is justified since it is good for their system. A variety of practices are employed, many of them direct and harsh—exhortation, reward and punishment techniques, sensory, sleep or social impoverishment, persuasion, and the like. It is edifying to learn that strong emotional discharges for or against the political system are provoked and encouraged. In this period of excitation, suggestibility is heightened and established beliefs are more easily destroyed. New tenets, even beliefs opposite to those originally held, can be inculcated. Modern brainwashing methods depend less on physical violence and more on fomenting confusion, intense anxiety and on mobilizing guilt feelings. During the chaotic emotional state the introduction of false memories and ideas is possible, and they become fixed through repeated indoctrination. The victim is provided with an entirely new assumptive set.

It surprises people to read about an obviously absurd "confession" from a strong-willed prisoner after his confinement in some totalitarian jail. At the "trial" he does not appear to be under the influence of drugs or in any particular fear for his life. Even if he is released and deported, the instilled beliefs linger on for a time. The success of persuasion, hyperemotional abreactions and conditioning in revising long-held beliefs is impressive. It is a weird demonstration of the fact that attitudes can change and can change rapidly.

Psychotherapy, in contrast, is an effort to change attitudes and behavior in a direction which is good for the patient and permits him to live more successfully according to the value system of his culture as interpreted by his therapist. It has developed more indirect and subtle techniques—suggestion, insight, counseling, abreaction, the transference relationship, and the like. Both techniques employ suggestion to achieve their goal especially, during the abreaction, which is recognized as a hypersuggestible period.

From what has been said to this point, the question whether drugs like LSD could favorably influence the psychotherapeutic process can be split into two parts. First, can it accelerate learning? Second, may it provide a basis for rapid personality change by providing a profound emotional experience?

When the hallucinogens are used within the framework of conventional psychotherapy their proponents make the following claims:

1. They reduce the patient's defensiveness and allow repressed memories and conflictual material to come forth. The recall of these events is improved and the abreaction is intense.

2. The emerging material is better understood because the patient sees the conflict as a visual image or in

vivid visual symbols. It is accepted without being overwhelming because the detached state of awareness makes the emerging guilt feelings less devastating.

3. The patient feels closer to the therapist and it is easier for him to express his irrational feelings.

4. Alertness is not impaired and insights are retained after the drug has worn off.

Under skilled treatment procedures, the hallucinogens do seem to produce these effects and one more which is not often mentioned. That is a marked heightening of the patient's suggestibility. Put in another way, the judgmental attitude of the patient toward the experience itself is diminished. This can be helpful, for insights are accepted without reservations and seem much more valid than under nondrug conditions.

The part of the self that doubts, the observing ego, is in abeyance; the striking happenings and their interpretation by the therapist takes on a "realer than real" significance. An overwhelming conviction in the value of the experience is felt. It is difficult to assess the contribution of suggestion to the psychotherapeutic effect of LSD, but it must be considerable. The therapeutic value of suggestion ought not be minimized. Although it is a "superficial" manipulation, it is a potent one. Suggestion and persuasion are part of every form of psychotherapy; under LSD their impact becomes a major feature of the procedure.

The previously mentioned enhancement of insightful recall and the emotional reliving of ancient traumas is a helpful take-off point for personality alteration. They by no means insure that beneficial changes will take place, but they facilitate the work to be done. Too many LSD therapists stop after the enormous insights and impressive abreactions have occurred. Actually, this point is really the start, not the end, of the re-educational process. After a patient has clearly seen himself for what he is, neither the sight nor the insight guarantees that he will be different in the future. One criticism of much LSD therapy is that the spectacular catharsis is considered sufficient to do the job. Most frequently, it produces a temporary period of glowing well-being, only to be followed by a gradual return to the old ways. Only a small number can, unassisted, use the dramatic events as a take-off point for progressive personality growth.

The difficult and more laborious process of relearning must still be undertaken and we have no evidence yet that this can be shortened with a drug like LSD. The desire to change may increase after one has clearly seen the burden under which one struggles, but hard, slow work still remains.

On the other hand, alterations of one's system of values can be rather rapid. One or very few LSD therapeutic experiences may modify the pressures of an overburdened conscience. By altering even for a few hours the habitual way of looking at ourselves, we might discover that the gnawing guilt was not due to a realistic transgression, but to the distortions of a relentless, punishing superego. After the patient has taken a penetrating look at an alienated, misdirected life, he may still manage to acquire some degree of self-acceptance with a reduction in remorse. Many patients have an unrealistically low estimate of themselves; an increase in their self-esteem is most desirable. These superego manipulations are all that can be accomplished for some individuals. The decompression of the guilt-ridden may not only lighten their load, but can also improve their interpersonal relationships by making the subjects easier to live with.

Jackson sees psychotherapeutic value in the LSD experience as a new beginning—an existential encounter of decisive proportions to be followed by a realignment of the perceptual set. He believes that the LSD encounter can lead to character restructuring. Patients are apt to describe death and rebirth experiences during the period of drug activity. It is the rigid, punishing superego that dies and then is reborn free of the old guilt. It is a new start with the slate wiped clean. No doubt the process represents the use of strong denial, but this defense might be preferable to the previous manner of handling feelings of shame and self-condemnation.

A course of LSD for uncovering purposes is ideally given by a skilled, devoted psychiatrist to a suitable patient whom he knows very well from prior non-LSD interviews. The therapist should be familiar from personal experience with the nature of the changes that the drug induces. He must be flexible enough to use whatever psychotherapeutic techniques are suitable to the situation, which is much more intense than conventional therapy. The months following the LSD treatments are most important, to provide an opportunity for the client's retraining process.

Unfortunately these requirements are not always met; certain LSD practitioners are far from qualified. They have been attracted to the procedure because it is novel and spectacular, or because it puts the therapist in an omniscient position. The best of psychotherapists can obtain excellent results using almost any psychiatric system. They are therefore not inclined to revise their therapeutic technique. The unsuccessful ones are more likely to try every new approach, in the hope that the method will remedy their shortcomings. But more important, the LSD technique is so dramatic and powerful that it fills whatever occult needs some therapists may have to be a mighty, all-powerful figure. Such therapists can hardly be expected to guide their patients toward psychological maturity when they themselves have major unresolved problems. The "miraculous" result they obtain with LSD is the "honeymoon" effect that follows massive abreaction, the shattering death-rebirth ordeal with superego decompression. All too often the treatment terminates at what is really the starting point.

An evaluation of the role of LSD as an aid to depth psychotherapy cannot be scrupulously made now. The capable practitioners who use LSD seem to be able to help their patients through a reconstructive analysis quite successfully and at an accelerated rate. The activities of the "fringe" therapists make a sober estimate of its place as an aid to treatment difficult. The more spectacular claims of instantaneous character transformation must be looked upon as conversions from one defensive repertoire to another—for example, from obsessiveness to denial and sublimation. These are the "cures" we read about in the Sunday supplements or hear about at cocktail parties. It must be restated that such shifts in the way life stress is handled can reduce tension and relieve such symptoms as impotence or psychogenic pain. It is like the lady who converts to Christian Science and trades her neurotic dyspepsia for a symptom-free sublimation of her troubles. This is fine until her appendix ruptures. Similarly, the patient who has had a transforming view of himself and the world through LSD may no longer see himself as worthless and the world as menacing. He can drop his guarded suspicious manner and become more open and outgoing. The hostility of others can be handled with denial. This is fine, provided the effect persists and is never fractured by events which cannot be ignored.

The adoption of a kindlier, more trusting approach to life by the LSD patient may in itself alter the attitudes of those with whom he interacts. They feel less threatened and insecure than when they are met with distrust. Thus the good feelings reverberate back and forth, converting the old, bitter world into a more amiable one. The patient's new adjustment is rewarded and reinforced. In this manner even a simple restructuring of the ego defenses can come to have a substantial and cumulative effect on the person and his problems. He has remade the old hostile environment into a benign one. The contribution of LSD in this instance is to substitute a less painful method of coping with existence, which is subsequently strengthened by a rewarding feedback from the environment. Jackson points out that when the immediate family is unwilling or unable to accept and foster the patient's new attitude toward them, it will be nullified and the patient will be worse off than before.

Some patients are completely unsuitable for a trial with the LSD type of therapy. The eternal adolescent who has never grown up or functioned effectively is a poor candidate. The extremely depressed, the hysterical and the paranoid personalities are poor risks because of the danger of accentuating their depressive, hysterical or paranoid tendencies. Although occasional claims have been made that psychotic patients have been helped, the consensus is that LSD is not for them. The borderline psychotic is a precarious patient because of the danger that he may decompensate and fall into a full-blown psychosis.

Ideally the LSD candidate will have the intelligence to understand the nature of the treatment and will have a strong desire to change. He should be willing to face and deal with considerable emotional pain during this more intensive treatment. The idea that the LSD phase is a beginning, not an end, of treatment must be acceptable to him.

People suffering from an excessively strict conscience, those who have lost confidence and self-esteem, and those who are unable to overcome the grief of a personal loss are the best candidates. Generally depressions due to situational factors are favorably influenced. Those "lost" people who are unable to find meaning in existence are particularly good candidates. Patients with anxiety or problems of passivity or agressivity are amenable to treatment. Sandison claims that the psychopathic character disorders can be helped by LSD treatment. Sexual psychopaths and drug addicts have been given courses of LSD with some benefit. The problem of the chronic alcoholic will be considered separately.

The techniques of using LSD for uncovering therapy vary widely. After the general problem areas have become known to the therapist, the first LSD interview may be started with a small dose (perhaps 25 micrograms) to give the patient a feeling of what the drug does. The dose is raised by small increments in subsequent sessions. Only rarely are more than 150 micrograms needed for this type of therapy.

The effects of LSD last four hours even with the smallest doses and more than eight hours with the larger amounts. The protection of the patient requires hospital facilities and constant supervision by the therapist or another suitable person. These precautions, far from alarming the patient, reassure him that he will be cared for and protected.

The therapist has a more strenuous role to play than under ordinary treatment procedures. It is not only that the sessions last all day, but his active participation is required from time to time. For certain patients "letting go" is the most difficult part of the procedure. It means a surrendering of the façade, a giving up of the rationalizations, and a willingness to face up to what must be faced. The evasive maneuvers of the LSD patient are numerous and deceptive. He may try to intellectualize the experience to avoid the confrontation with himself. Conscious or unconscious efforts to suppress the drug effects are sometimes attempted. He may divert the therapist with somatic complaints or with fascinating descriptions of the visual wonders, a sort of flight into beauty. Delaying tactics of all sorts have been attempted. Instead of penetrating into crucial problem areas, the patient may try to skirt around them. An important part of the therapist's job is to identify the evasions and to concentrate on the ordeal of unswerving self-examination. He must insist that the material, overwhelming as it is, be completely dealt with. At the same time he must provide support and reassurance during the ordeal. It is a sort of "dig and fill" operation—an uncovering phase followed by a resolving and supporting phase. The patient cannot be allowed to flee from the frightening symbolism that comes up. If he does, there is danger of a period of psychotic disorganization. It is impressive how the terror disappears once the patient goes into the horrifying symbol and comes to grips with it.

A frequent question is, "How real are the LSD memories, how relevant is the symbolism that comes forth?" The memories may be completely accurate or they can be screen memories, protective memories which distort the actual event, and therefore less valid. Some memories may not represent events that actually happened but may symbolize underlying wishes or drives. The symbolism can be cast in abstractions, in the image of the person whose relationship is being considered or in strange, remote settings. Not infrequently feelings about the important people in the patient's life are projected onto the therapist, and his features and expression are then described as resembling them.

The common belief among psychotherapists that repressed memories for traumatic events must be released only over a prolonged period of time, and then with great care and trepidation, should be reconsidered. Under LSD the most devastating of buried memories have been recovered and within a single session thoroughly relived and resolved. It requires courage by the patient and fortitude by the therapist, but it can be accomplished within hours. Perhaps it is the peculiar state of detachment or depersonalization which permits the LSD patient to exhume excruciating memories and, while reliving them, also be a calm observer to the events. Or, it may be the length of the session which permits the more intensive working through of the material.

Repetition is a valuable device for reducing the emotional load on recalled conflicts. Once the meaning comes to be understood, it is dealt with again and again, until it ceases to evoke an emotional response. Tape recordings of valuable sessions are used to re-expose the patient on future occasions.

A number of psychotherapists have used LSD in a group setting. Under these circumstances an intensified interaction and rapport between the participants is achieved, and the sessions tend to be more "gutty." Groups of hospitalized sexual deviates and of alcoholics have been studied. The use of LSD makes the proceedings more directly confronting and emotionally loaded. "Phoniness" on the part of the participants is quickly identified and rejected by the members of the group.

An unbiased careful study of the therapeutic effects of LSD on patients observed for a number of years after cessation of treatment would be highly desirable, but the difficulties of executing such a project are prodigious. It has already been mentioned that the therapist must believe in his brand of therapy if favorable results are to be expected. Naturally those who have faith in their type of therapy will be biased in their judgments of patient improvement. The patient himself is not necessarily a good judge of the therapeutic effect. The mere fact that he feels better does not necessarily mean that desirable changes have occurred. The goals of emotional growth are many, and their measurement is most difficult. For a proper study it would seem necessary to have a second set of impartial psychiatrists evaluate the patient for evidence of improvement, using predefined criteria.

The difficulties of doing a clear-cut study would be far from solved even with these precautions. A control group of patients matched as well as possible with the LSD patients must be given the identical treatment except that LSD is not used. A placebo or drug with some minor activity identical in appearance would have to be substituted. It is quite impossible to keep the therapist in the dark about who is getting the LSD because of its pronounced action. Will he invest as much energy and dedication to his non-LSD patients? The patients themselves will quickly know whether they have received LSD or not. Their expectations of its benefits will alter their therapeutic set. These difficulties and others are the reasons why a decisive test of the efficacy of LSD has not yet been performed. The problems are great but surmountable. Hopefully, this investigation will be done one day.

To state that other psychotherapies in current usage have not been exposed to a similar vigorous experimental survey is beside the point. Psychiatry has entered a stage of development in which every new treatment procedure will require stringent proof of its effectiveness, and the older ones will also come to be scrutinized more critically. Thorough and convincing investigations of the tranquilizing and antidepressant drugs and of electroshock treatment have already been done to determine their relative values.

The second question is whether personality change can come about with LSD rapidly, safely and with some possibility of enduring. In this context change does not refer to the detailed examination of past relationships and attitudes so that they can be understood and worked through but consists of a sudden new look at oneself and the universe and a decision to abruptly alter the approach to the old problems.

Consider a man who had been living alone all his life in a private emotional fortress, busily engaged in deepening the moats and strengthening the parapets. Despite the prodigious defenses he still feels unprotected and insecure. Furthermore, the walls are now so high that he has separated himself from people. He can only shout to them from the battlements and cannot quite make out what they are shouting back, but the sounds are unfriendly. One day a tremendous storm destroys his stronghold. He is defenseless. To his great surprise he is not demolished or even attacked. People seem friendly. What had he feared? His own hostility? Why was he never loved? Was it those impregnable walls? Maybe it would be better to trust and rejoin the human race than retreat behind the barriers again.

A rapid personality conversion of this sort can happen spontaneously and without warning in the form of a religious experience, as described by William James in *Varieties of Religious Experience.* Another type can be induced in a revivalist's tent by the fervid preaching of an evangelist. With proper preparation and guidance, drugs like LSD will also evoke this state. When it is chemically produced, it is called a psychedelic experience. The necessary elements are a stirring emotional encounter sufficient to change one's established values and the resolution to act upon the revelation. All degrees of confidence are placed in the event, from mild surmise to absolute certainty in the truth of the message. When credence is high, the need to change is great, and when the "significant other" rewards and supports the change, the possibility of an enduring conversion is favorable. Evangelical "cures" are too often impermanent because the incomplete conviction gained cannot withstand the harsh scrape of everyday living. Even spontaneous religious experiences which seem to have been divinely inspired may not resist the corrosion of disbelief and sabotage by the person closest to the convert. The transformation wrought by the psychedelic experience is subject to the same fate. In a favorable, rewarding environment it will flourish; inexorable punishment can destroy it.

The psychedelic technique fulfills the hopes of many troubled individuals for a magical intervention, a quick solution to their problems. For those who are unable or unwilling to undergo the major overhaul, a psychedelic resolution of this sort might be a feasible procedure.

There are hazards. If a person has seen the glory and goodness of life via psychedelics and then backslides, the guilt of failure is added to the hopelessness of his situation. The depression may be deeper than before the treatment. Others who have been touched by the Light may develop so unrealistic a view of themselves and the world that they become most difficult to live with. These hazards demonstrate the need for counseling even when the psychedelic technique is employed.

The psychedelic type of psychotherapy has been administered to more chronic alcoholics than to any other diagnostic category. There are good reasons for this large proportion. The current estimate of problem alcoholics has been put at five million in the United States alone, and the supply is not diminishing. As a group alcoholics are disinclined to stay with a program of long-term psychotherapy. The recovery rate without treatment is very low (4 per cent), and established treatments are far from cures. For those who can stay in Alcoholics Anonymous, the sobriety rate is understood to exceed 50 per cent, but unfortunately this agency can reach only a minority of the total alcoholic population. The end stages of uncontrollable drinking are so deplorable that any measure that offers a possibility of success ought to be tried. Since the degree of drinking is something that can be estimated more easily than can personality change, one formidable problem—the evaluation of results—is eliminated. Although sobriety itself is not the highest of goals, nothing can be accomplished with the alcoholic patient unless he maintains sobriety.

While it may be rash to generalize about the causes of alcoholism or the personality of the alcoholic, perhaps something ought to be said about these matters. Alcohol has been defined as the liquid in which the superego is soluble. It may be even more of a universal solvent for our civilization than that. Some portions of ego function also dissolve in this socially acceptable form of surcease. Not only do the sense of responsibility, pride and self-respect melt away, but anxiety, depression, timidity and restraint also liquefy. Savage points out a further reason for the current epidemic of dipsomania. The drunk of an earlier era might have been drowning his sorrows; the modern drunk is filling the emptiness of his existence. It is the loss of purpose and meaning, the increasing alienation from life, that pushes many of our contemporaries into alcoholic excess. Many years ago William James suggested that one possible cause of alcoholism was the hope of finding something "out there," a search for a bit of a mystical experience. If this is so, the alcoholic is doomed to almost certain failure. He may get a flash of it in the instant before stupor prevails, but usually even that is denied him.

Alcohol is a valuable social item, and its moderate and even sporadically immoderate use is by no means decried here. It can procure feelings of friendliness, good cheer and relaxation. Some people want this aid to gaiety, gregariousness and well-being, and no reason exists why it should not be available to social drinkers.

As is the case with all psychochemicals, it is the

difficulties of self-dosage which bring most alcoholics to heel. Those with the greatest unfulfilled needs and those who are seeking oblivion are the most vulnerable to the loss of dosage control. It may take many years of heavy drinking, but eventually the addiction is established. Efficiency is impaired, jobs are lost, assets are wasted, families are split and health is broken. At this point guilt over the ruin that he has brought about and the sense of helplessness and hopelessness compound the alcoholic's reasons to drink. To attempt to rescue and rehabilitate an end-stage alcoholic can be a disappointing and formidable task. It is only rarely accomplished by the individual himself.

The notion that the drunk must hit bottom before he can be saved is well known and has implications for LSD therapy. "Hitting bottom" has a number of facets. It is usually brought on by a jolting disaster. The wife finally packs up and leaves, or the victim wakes up on Skid Row in DTs. It is usually the first occasion in which he unreservedly admits that he is a drunk. The admission is important, for it may start him looking for help in earnest. It is the point at which he realizes that he cannot go on; Tiebout calls it self-surrender. He gives up the inadequate positions of denial and rationalization and is finally willing to seek help from some external source. This may be found in religion (James suggested that religio-mania was a cure for dipsomania), A.A. or psychotherapy. Smith believed that some of his LSD-treated alcoholics experienced an artificial "hitting bottom" which was followed by marked improvement in the drinking pattern of half of his patients.

Some anthropologic evidence is available that hallucinogens used in a religious setting can combat alcoholism. The American Indians were a defeated people during the nineteenth century, deprived of their way of life, refugees in their own land. Too many of their number took to firewater. Most of those who later joined the peyote religion gave up whiskey. Obviously, the reformation was not due to peyote alone. It was the therapeutic combination of a faith, group solidarity and the ceremonial use of the drug.

LSD is generally utilized in a specific way when it is given to severe alcoholics for psychedelic therapy. The dose is much higher (200 to 600 micrograms) than when it is employed for uncovering therapy, and only one or very few treatments are given. The aim is to achieve a profound transcendental experience. The massive amount of the drug defeats any possibility that the ego defenses will hold off psychic dissociation. A psychotic disorganization can be avoided by establishing a field of trust in the procedure and the participants. At the peak of the reaction the boundaries of the ego are lost, and a strong sense of unity with the world outside is felt. What is seen and felt are complementary to the egoless state. A new awareness of one's relatedness to others and to the universe is strengthened because the reality of these feelings is totally accepted. One's concept of self is drastically altered. The hopeless, sinful derelict is now an identity with meaning and worth. Experience becomes discontinuous. A break is made between the miserable past and the hopeful future. The old mess is over. It is a resurrection, rebirth, a new beginning. The rules of life have suddenly been changed.

What has happened? Obviously the "bad" superego has been demolished and replaced by a "good," nonpunitive one, thus reducing the load. The strong conviction of belonging and of having a personal worth gives new meaning to the outer world and changes the perception of it. The drunk no longer has sorrows to drown, nor is his existence empty. The enormity of the experience, the total confirmation, in that it was all intensely seen, the clarity and "reality" of what was felt, all combine to break up the existing pattern of behavior.

Technically, this phenomenon can be analyzed in terms of an enormous use of denial mechanisms, superego introjects and regression. This is helpful, but another consideration is even more pertinent: can the experience actually produce abstinence in the severe alcoholic? The answer, as might be expected is not capable of being reduced to a straightforward yes or no.

The half-dozen or so reports of the use of psychedelic therapy for the alcoholic indicate that over half the patients are considered much improved. The period of follow-up observation varies from a couple of months to a few years. The fact that the evaluators are enthusiastic believers in their method and that the studies are not controlled must be taken into account in appraising them. What seems established is that a certain number of confirmed alcoholics will actually stop drinking for years following this treatment and are able to rehabilitate themselves. Another group relapses immediately or after a period of time. It is an important matter to find out the precise results of this relatively short treatment over many years and what factors make for success and failure.

It is easy to be critical and say that only a faith cure is involved. It is true that nothing is changed—except that the patient has achieved a new faith, reinforced by the overwhelming experience of his sense and his senses. Faith can move mountains, faith can also stop a man's drinking for a lifetime—or a day.

10 The Dangers to the Patient— and the Therapist

Is there a price to pay for a sudden, steep plunge into the depths of the unconscious? Or does the mind have inbuilt stabilizing mechanisms which keep one from drowning in the waters of irreality? Enormous psychic descents have been described here; what disasters can befall the explorer?

Four years ago these questions impelled me to write to sixty-two European and North American investigators who had published papers on the human use of mescaline or LSD. To that time little had been printed about the complications that might result when the hallucinogens were administered as either research or therapeutic tools. Forty-four replies were received—a rather good response to a questionnaire sent to overworked people.

The information was then compiled and analyzed. It was found to represent the experience gained from using the two drugs on slightly more than 25,000 occasions, on about 5,000 people. Each person had received LSD or mescaline from one to eighty times. The doses ranged from 25 to 1500 micrograms for LSD and 200 to 1200 milligrams for mescaline.

It had been suggested to the respondents that the returned questionnaire need not be signed, in order to obtain information on mishaps with which the investigator might prefer not to be identified. In every instance the returned data sheets were signed, and often an accompanying letter went into valuable details.

In the survey no serious physical complications were reported. A single coronary occlusion which occurred a few days after an LSD exposure was interpreted as coincidental. It was interesting to note that even when the drugs had been given to Skid Row alcoholics whose general health, and particularly their liver functions, were impaired, no physical complications were observed.

A number of the side effects that developed during the actual period of the drugs' activity were collected. These complaints were not frequent but occurred with sufficient regularity to be attributed to the drugs. Physical discomfort, including nausea, vomiting, aches and pains, has already been mentioned. Anxiety and panic states were noted, particularly during the struggle to maintain control of the situation. Occasionally a patient became frightened toward the end of a session because of his distorted time perception; imagined that he had been in the state so long that he would never get back. In contrast, others became somewhat depressed with the waning effects and the realization that they were return-

ing from a blissful world into a vexing one. Unmanage-
ability of the subject or patient was encountered at least
once by most of the respondents. This developed when
the individual completely lost his grasp of the situation
and acted upon some paranoid notion. If he were
unprotected, he might run off or accidentally hurt
himself. Those in attendance were almost never as-
saulted. When a "sitter" was not present, the unmanage-
able subject might get involved in a predicament which
was at least embarrassing or at most dangerous. Disrob-
ing was sporadically mentioned, curiously enough in
connection with the ecstatic states.

During the days immediately following the drug
exposure, certain undesirable effects were seen. One was
a prolongation of the hallucinogenic state for twenty-
four to forty-eight hours beyond the usual time of
termination. These were psychoticlike episodes with
agitation and visual aberrations which subsided with
psychiatric assistance or tranquilizing medication. Another possibility, especially when mescaline was used,
was the transient recurrence of the reaction days or
months afterward. Some of these recrudescences were
momentary and pleasant, others lasted for minutes or
hours and were often construed as distressing. The latter
was prone to appear following a period of physical or
mental exhaustion.

Major or prolonged psychological complications were
almost never described in the group of experimental
subjects who had been selected for their freedom from
mental disturbances. No case of attempted or completed
suicide and only one instance of a psychotic reaction

lasting more than two days was reported. When patients were given these drugs for therapeutic purposes, however, the untoward reactions were somewhat more frequent. Prolonged psychotic states occurred in one out of every 550 patients. These breakdowns happened to individuals who were already emotionally ill; some had sustained schizophrenic breaks in the past. In certain instances the unskillful management of the patient contributed to the undesirable outcome.

As an example, one patient with considerable anxiety, many phobias and disabling ruminations about his body functions was given LSD on three occasions. During one session he saw in great detail that when he was four years old he had smothered his baby brother who had been crying. There had been no previous awareness of the event, only a vague feeling that something bad had happened when he was very young. The impact was so strong that the next day he went to the police and confessed. After an investigation the "murder" could not be confirmed and the patient was not detained. Nevertheless, he remained very upset, agitated and depressed and committed himself to a mental hospital. It took one year for him to recover sufficiently to be discharged. A number of errors were evident in this patient's treatment. To begin with, as an incipient schizophrenic, he was a poor risk for LSD. It was predictable that such a difficult patient would need complete support and assistance from the therapist. This was not forthcoming. The highly traumatic memory, which probably was symbolic of his hatred of the new arrival who had appropriated his mother's affection, should have been dealt with as it arose. This was not done.

Serious depressions culminating in attempted or completed suicides were rare complications. One patient in 830 was unsuccessful and one in 2,500 was successful in efforts at self-destruction. The exact relationship between the suicide attempt and the drug experience was far from clear in most instances. When a direct relationship could be seen, it was due to devastating insights which were not skillfully managed.

The suicidal act tended to occur weeks after the end of an unsuccessful course of treatment. Depression over the failure of the LSD to provide the anticipated relief may have been contributory. Other factors unrelated to the drug also played a role. Although extremely rare, suicide is a real danger with any type of therapy which attempts to treat patients with grave emotional disturbances. This complication is a risk during LSD treatment, especially in haphazardly handled or unprotected patients.

At the time this review of the dangers of LSD and mescaline was compiled, no instances of addiction to these drugs were reported, nor was their social misuse mentioned. However, even then the tendency of unstable, antisocial individuals to be attracted to the euphoric aspects of the drug experience was pointed out. A number of precautions were recommended, consisting of careful selection of patients and subjects, their complete protection including the constant attendance of an experienced person, and the requirement that the therapist be responsible and expert in the techniques of using LSD and of managing its complications. It was concluded that, properly employed, the dangers could be minimized, and the continued use of the drugs as research tools was indicated. When they are employed as adjuncts to psychotherapy, certain additional risks must be accepted.

In the four years since that report was written, the situation has changed. Hallucinogens have come into wider, more casual use and a subsequent increase in complications have been seen. Dr. Keith Ditman and I have collected a series of instances which demonstrate some of the difficulties to be expected when the hallucinogens are improperly utilized. These undesirable reactions were not searched out, they were referred to us because our interest in LSD was known. Two quite new developments have appeared; unskilled dispensers of the drugs have emerged, and a black market in these substances is now flourishing. It is from these sources that most of the mishaps reported in detail in the May, 1963, issue of the *Archives of General Psychiatry* were obtained.

We have seen a number of patients in either prepsychotic states or involved in definite psychotic breaks following LSD. One such patient was a secretary to a therapist with a large LSD practice. When interviewed by us she said that she had taken the drug between 200 and 300 times during the past three years, singly or in combination with other hallucinogens, stimulants and sedatives. At first the drug experiences had been pleasant and helpful in "unblocking" her. Later they became very scary and left her unable to control her emotions.

She appeared panicky, unable to think clearly, and fearful of the recurrent visual hallucinations which were like those seen under LSD, such as the skulls of people she knew moving around the room. She had to take large doses of sedatives to quiet her during the day and to procure sleep at night. The extraordinarily frequent administration of hallucinogens and the other drugs for quasitherapeutic purposes apparently account for her difficulties. Similar instances have been seen where one or a few LSD exposures of the wrong patient by the wrong doctor has ended in a similar disturbance. Four other patients have been interviewed who also complained that LSD-like hallucinations formed part of their distressing aftereffects.

A ten-year-old boy accidentally consumed a sugar cube containing LSD which his father, a detective, had confiscated from a "pusher." The child had a severe reaction for several days, which gradually became less upsetting but did not completely subside. A week afterward he was still nervous, especially when he saw movements on the TV screen when the set was not on. When he tried to study, the words in his books would waver. He was treated with a combination of psychotherapy and tranquilizers and made a full recovery in six weeks.

Psilocybin, LSD, peyote and morning glory seeds have been added to the drug repertoire of "beat" circles looking for offbeat experiences. These antisocial characters north and south of the border were already involved with alcohol, marihuana, sleeping pills, wake-up pills, demerol and heroin. They are multihabituated: they use these drugs and others consecutively or in combination. When such a potent drug as LSD is added to their diet, catastrophes can be predicted. They have occurred.

Although true addiction has still not been recorded, it can be definitely stated that habituation to the psychological effects of this group of drugs is possible in certain personality types. Passive-dependent and psychopathic individuals with access to large supplies have taken them uncounted times and have had difficulty in breaking themselves of the habit. Precise information on the number who have become habituated is impossible to obtain.

The paranoid person has been mentioned as unsuitable for LSD therapy. When he receives a drug of the lysergic acid group to bring on a psychedelic experience, a latent grandiosity can become manifest. LSD dislodges the skeptic in us, and conjectures become certainties. During the period of ego dissolution the feelings of unity, rebirth and redemption may not culminate in a feeling of humble gratitude; the paranoid person may conclude from his experience that he has been chosen to lead others into this real reality. He can gain considerable gratification from his power to bestow a religious experience on his disciples. Small psychedelic sects have already formed and they have a magnetic attraction for both the gullible and the seekers after "kicks." These extremely potent drugs are declared to be everybody's birthright and their regulation a ruse to maintain power in the hands of the medical monopoly or governmental agencies. At a recent professional meeting, a Canadian

psychologist said, "I would like to foresee in the next
couple of decades that LSD could be obtained from gum
machines in any drugstore to any person who had a
penny." It is difficult to believe that such credulity
exists.

It has become evident that the practitioner who deals
with agents which induce a highly vulnerable state must
use them with the greatest of care and integrity. Ricks
writes that the drugs have been enlisted not only for
consciousness expansion, but also for consciousness sus-
pension, as an "aid to seductions, and other manipulations of an extremely messy and unpleasant sort." The
unethical practitioners and the omnipotent sect leaders
have been the main factors in the rise of the black-
market operation by their sweeping claims and insist-
ence that LSD is something grand for everyone. At
present the illegal commerce in LSD, mescaline and
psilocybin is concentrated in the larger cities and some
of the university campuses. LSD is peddled in pills,
ampules and sugar cubes saturated with 100 micrograms.
A suspicion persists that some of the clandestine material
is either contaminated or mixed with other substances
because extremely disturbed reactions have occurred.
These chemicals are not overly difficult for a determined
analytic chemist to manufacture; their source must stem
from more than one basement laboratory. Newspaper
items reveal that large amounts of LSD and precursors
to LSD have been confiscated from a number of separate
sources. At the going market price of from $1 to $10 a
sugar cube, the profits must be very attractive.

Some of the young in mind who obtain the black-market material will casually take it under dubious conditions and without the necessary controls. Sooner or later they will find themselves caught in the grip of pure horror. With LSD the "kicks" can go both ways. Other people will be given LSD without their knowledge, by design or accident, and will suffer the shattering belief that they are going mad. A suicide resulting from such an event has already been described in the psychiatric literature.

Most of the recent sufferers from complications whom we studied had obtained LSD from improper sources. The authorized manufacturer had already cut off supplies to those workers who were not using the drug under the recommended precautions. But this was no deterrent to those who wanted to continue its use. They proceeded to obtain supplies from Mexico, other foreign countries or the black market.

A strange malady which has not yet been described elsewhere is an affliction, not of the receiver, but of the giver of the hallucinogens. This peculiar disorder might be called therapist breakdown. An unusual number of those dispensing these drugs have themselves come down with psychiatric disturbances. Research personnel seem immune to the disease: it is the therapist or quasitherapist who suffer the affliction. The manifestations are variable. After intensive, though sometimes only after brief, contact with the drugs, a few have gone on to a psychotic breakdown or to megalomaniacal ideas of grandeur. Marked depressions and even a suicide in which these agents played a role are known. A couple of practitioners have found themselves in legal difficulties because of antisocial practices. This is an impressive morbidity, in view of the relatively small number of American practitioners using the hallucinogens. It constitutes a substantial minority of those dispensing the drugs. Of course, not all are stricken. The majority of therapists using LSD remain intact and in good health.

How can it be that so many have fallen prey to these mental ailments? True, doctors also become patients, and psychiatrists and psychologists are not exempt from the very ills that they treat, but hardly in the numbers seen in those involved with the hallucinogenic drugs. When the instances of breakdown are scrutinized, three causative factors emerge. Some of the lay and professional therapists attracted to the spectacular aspects of the hallucinogens were not of first quality. They were unstable before involvement with LSD, and in one or two instances their mental states were only tenuously balanced. It was hardly surprising to find that this borderline group would develop emotional difficulties.

A second cause of this disorder is that the ability to induce the transcendental state is a heady and powerful endowment. Only well-adjusted therapists without personal needs to play God will be unaffected by the potency inherent in the situation. Those who have had latent notions of omniscience can become privately or expressly convinced of their own pre-eminence. Such an individual, with sufficient awareness of reality to keep his grandiose ideas hidden beneath a façade of meekness is a real threat to his clients. He can become quite successful in controlling small groups of people in the role of sect leader or lay therapist. The intensity of the sibling rivalry among the psychedelic prophets is striking. Such vehemence makes one suspect that their own drug experience had not cured them of the baser emotions.

A third reason for the high incidence of therapist breakdown is that certain dispensers of these potions also have consumed them in fabulous amounts. One hears of individuals who have performed hundreds of self-experiments with mystifying combinations of psychochemicals. Naturally they encounter the same adverse reactions as any other unwise user. The human pharmacology of prolonged, excessive indulgence in the hallucinogenic drugs is unknown. However, Hoffer suspects that many hundreds of exposures to the hallucinogenic indoles might leave permanent residuals.

The marginal purveyor of hallucinogens did little to advance our knowledge in this important field. His approach was invariably casual and prejudiced. In fact, his activities repelled qualified investigators from entering into careful evaluations of the clinical potential of these drugs. He caused pressures to be brought on the competent therapists already involved in sound studies. As a result, the distribution and regulation of these agents has become much more stringent, and new restrictive legislation is being studied.

There are many reminders which teach us that the sober evaluation of drugs or techniques of possible value have been abandoned when their reputation was soiled. Hypnosis was relegated to a scientific limbo for half a century because of the lurid claims of Mesmerists and its esoteric usage on the vaudeville stage and the front parlor. Only in recent years has it begun to be seriously investigated. If such drugs as LSD are taken over by beat and immature elements and sensational tales of cures and disasters stream from the news media, responsible researchers will become disaffected and move out of the field.

It should not be necessary to repeat the errors of the past, but it seems inevitable that we will. Three centuries ago opium was hailed as a harmless panacea. After uncounted numbers were caught up in a compulsion to take a daily tipple of the juice of the poppy, a new chemical discovery was enthusiastically offered as a cure for opium addiction. Its name was heroin.

Hashish is a drug which merits detailed psycho-pharmacologic investigation. Nevertheless, because of its miserable reputation, almost no research is being conducted with hashish or its cannabinols. It remains to be seen whether the recent astonishing and sensational publicity in connection with the psychedelics will repel responsible scientists from pursuing their investigations.

This is the harm that can come from the irresponsible and the credulous. The dangers are not only to the person, but also to the accumulation of knowledge about the mind, information which has important implications.

That strict controls are necessary is unquestionable. It is to be hoped that the public and the legislators, upset by the goings-on of a few, will not insist upon laws which will make further explorations of LSD and like drugs impossible. What must be remembered is that it is not the legal supplies which are causing the mischief; these are now tightly restricted. It is the bootlegged material that is being carelessly and sometimes dangerously misused.

Lest this long list of the encountered complications give the impression of complete condemnation of these agents, it must be restated that when under proper administration they are quite safe. If drugs are given to emotionally healthy groups for research investigations, the dangers are insignificant. When the drugs are carefully used by able psychiatrists on selected patients for therapeutic purposes, the risks are slightly greater but may not exceed those of other treatment procedures. Nor is therapist breakdown a hazard to the stable physician who uses LSD for his patients' needs, not his own.

If it is evident that on occasion the taker of psychedelic chemicals can be imperiled, there are hazards for the giver as well. To poke into the subcortical recesses of the brain with potent molecules has its hazards as well as its enchantments. In any case, these concoctions present us with a precarious choice, if not a danger, and on this point everyone is involved, takers and non-takers alike.

The question is whether drugs like LSD should be incorporated into our society. Specifically; should chemically-induced self-transcendence, ecstasy and ego dissolution be available to all who seek it? Should we have the freedom to alter our awareness drastically? Do we have the inalienable right to expand our consciousness?

Relatively minor changes in consciousness by means

of chemicals are unrestricted by law and custom. We can freely alert ourselves with coffee, tea or some of the lesser stimulants. Certain degrees of loosening one's psychological inhibitions or deturmoilizing oneself are widely practiced in the home or at the bar. Traditionally, more profound derangements or re-arrangements of consciousness are considered medical prerogatives. It is well known, however, that fair numbers of folks who yearn to get outside ordinary consciousness for a while will take almost anything to accomplish this. To sniff gasoline or airplane glue, to eat large quantities of nutmeg or datura are crude and stumbling efforts. The current deliriant in fashion in England now is "blue velvet," a mixture of paregoric and pyribenzamine, while here the passing fancy is for "purple heart," a barbiturate-benzedrine mixture.

The hallucinogens are to these inept efforts as a Himalayan peak is to a sand hill—not only vaster and more challenging, but also more perilous. Should these agents be available to all who want to look down into the abyss from the summit in order to find themselves? What would the effects of freely available LSD be upon our way of life? Just how could it be introduced into our complex, modern existence?

At least one group, originally at Harvard, briefly in Mexico, and currently in the Catskills, have asserted that the psychedelics have momentous socio-political implications and that consciousness expansion on a wholesale basis is feasible and desirable. They say it could provide the means by which we will finally break through the endless, senseless, frustrating game we play, and divert the energies we now expend playing this comic tragedy called life in favor of a permanent state of self-transcendence. At last we would live in peace—with ourselves, with our environment and with all of humanity. The desirability of such self-realization is evident and not an impossibility. We know that an occasional individual, Buddha for example, does somehow spontaneously achieve a mental condition of complete loss of self, with a falling away of all worldly cares. It is not inconceivable that chemicals such as the ones we have been discussing might make accessible to the many what was formerly restricted to the very few. It is an attractive proposition to the harassed and discontented, the uncertain and the despondent.

The International Foundation for Internal Freedom (IFIF), with Timothy Leary as its mentor, appears to have made three efforts to fracture our tribal taboos against chemical transcendence. All three have been unsuccessful, but they are worthy of study. The first attempt was to pronounce that these agents were a food, a sort of cerebral vitamin which we all lacked, and as a consequence we suffered from a derangement of our ability to really see and really know. As a food, it was our birthright, and to restrict it was deliberate malnutrition by those in power. Aside from a complete absence of evidence that we suffer from a depletion of the hallucinogenic tryptamines, this appeal never achieved any support whatever. One reason for the lack of success of this approach was due to the fact that we live in a highly regulated society. What we swallow is controlled, and swallowed items that exert powerful activity upon the mind are called drugs, not foods. Drugs are now most carefully regulated and their legal procurement has become a problem.

At about this time, these drugs, predominantly psilocybin, were given to substantial numbers of influential people. Many converts were made, and satellite groups sprang up. Deliberate efforts to obtain wide publicity for the new and easy way to achieve a religious or mystical experience were disseminated. These activities also disturbed the less imaginative authorities and led to the Leary-Alpert departures from Harvard and Mexico. The attendant publicity turned out to have a mixed quality. Some articles were vividly enthusiastic, others reflected doubts about the odd characters involved, the hipster jargon and the casual precautions about the administration of The Experience.

One excellent method of changing one's culture in a rational society is to prove that the new is better than the old, just as it has been demonstrated that penicillin is better for pneumonia than bloodletting. IFIF also indulged in research activities. It was the sort of research that made scientists wince, but it was impressive enough for the uncritical. Their best known piece of work involved the rehabilitation of prisoners at a Massachusetts correctional facility through the use of psilocybin. Regrettably, it was bad research. Bad research is worse than no research, for it takes much tedious repetition to correct it. As "research" it conveys an aura of reliability, and eventually it comes to be quoted and requoted in publications as established fact. It is the curse of every science, especially the behavioral sciences.

A brief review of the IFIF research is worthwhile, for it demonstrates how easy it is to obtain findings which confirm one's own biases. A group of recidivist prisoners were given a series of psilocybin experiences. After an all too brief followup period, it was stated that the psilocybin group stayed out of jail much more successfully than other prisoners. If true, this is exciting and encouraging news, for it means that hardened criminals can be made law-abiding by a few psilocybin sessions given under the right conditions. An analysis of what was actually done makes this conclusion less impressive. Psilocybin treatments were not the only factor involved, but the selected group had the advantage of many other measures known to be therapeutic. Not only did the psilocybin group enjoy a special status while in prison, but they developed close and friendly relationships with the investigators. A special pre-parole course of instruction was established for them. They were given special assistance in obtaining housing and employment. They maintained their contacts with their buddies at Harvard. None of these benefits were available to the group of prisoners who were used for comparison. The evaluation of the results was not performed by impartial individuals, nor do we have a report of the longer-term behavior of the psilocybin treated group.

Perhaps it might be argued that the prisoners had such severe character disturbances that simply humanizing their environment, i.e. improving the non-drug factors, could hardly be important enough to keep them out of jail. This is assuredly not so. Groups such as A.A. or Synanon, using neither drugs nor professional assistance have rehabilitated impressive numbers of end-stage alcoholics and drug addicts with the same techniques of empathic group relationships which the Concord prison experiment employed as adjuncts to the psilocybin.

It is likely that use of psilocybin, plus increasing the prisoner's chances of establishing himself on the outside, would have demonstrated that the psilocybin group actually did better than a matched group of prisoners to whom only the supportive treatment was given. But we will never know how important the drug treatment itself really was until another study is done that carefully controls every variable but one—the administration of psilocybin. Such an experiment will be extremely difficult to perform, for the investigators will have to maintain the identical enthusiastic attitude toward the control group: help them, befriend them and try just as hard to keep them out of jail.

Much can be learned from the efforts of IFIF to introduce psychedelic chemicals into the American culture. The first striking impression is that these people, despite multiple contacts with the Greater Reality, did not demonstrate a wisdom capable of predicting the response to their various endeavors. It would seem to bear out the hypothesis that psychedelic experiences create an opportunity to grow and to learn, but as isolated events they do not assure automatic sagacity.

Another lesson that seems obvious is that any group wishing to change the way of life of its subculture must rigidly eliminate those borderline characters who lack the discipline to sacrifice, to endure, to work hard, and to maintain a practical knowledge of reality.

Furthermore, it is suspected that a permanent state of self-transcendence is probably neither desirable nor attainable. What is experienced in the visionary state must be brought back to our present condition and applied to the predicaments and perplexities of everyday life.

Some observers sincerely believe that Leary and his colleagues have something of significance to say. Theirs is not a new statement; it has been said by Sartre, by psychologists like Fromm, by philosophers like Teilhard de Chardin, by biologists like Julian Huxley, and by many others. It is, indeed, an ancient message, but it bears restating—for we are forever losing it.

The message is that we have forgotten or denied an essential aspect of our lives—the deep awareness of ourselves, and beyond the Self, the empathic feelings of relatedness to life and living. We have become too preoccupied with trivialities, possessions, status—the trappings rather than the substance of achievement. The trappings have trapped us in a welter of meaningless goals, trivial values, empty successes. It may not be necessary to know what our minute contribution to the tapestry of existence is, but we must never forget that we are a part of the whole.

It is because so many are unable to achieve this feeling of belonging that the psychedelic state seems so attractive. They sense that in it meaning can be found—meaning of a profundity beyond the pallid secularism and the all too comfortable religions of our day. They sense that greater significance, more sustaining values, more persisting relationships are possible than those at hand.

In the chemically procured mystical state a few find persuasive answers to their doubts. The answers are apprehended with such complete conviction that the certitude gained from the transcendent encounter makes the critical bystander aware of one further possible misuse of such experiences. It is not impossible that those who are made chemically credulous might be exploited by some unregenerated dispenser. So the possibilities for good and ill intertwine. Caution, therefore, rather than rashness seems most fitting in working out the future of the psychedelic substances.

11 *War Without Death*

One facet of the LSD story remains to be told. We have read the reports of the excursions into madness and mysticism, the discussions of its place in research, psychotherapy and creativeness and its uses for "kicks" and for social revolt. The combined amount of LSD made for all these purposes probably does not equal the quantity manufactured and stockpiled for a single project—psychochemical warfare.

What is written here is not derived from secret material. It is extrapolated from statements made to legislative committees, articles on CBR (chemical, bacteriological and radiological) warfare plus some knowledge of LSD's activity. It has been publicly acknowledged that the United States, the Soviet Union and other countries are studying the mass casualty-producing effects of this drug and others in the same category. Experiments have been performed on groups of soldiers given the drug without their knowledge. Dosage-response curves have been worked out. Methods of delivery as an aerosol spray from planes, a reservoir contaminant by saboteurs, and as a missile-delivered disabling agent have been studied. Attempts to devise defenses against these threats are also the concern of CBR research and development teams.

Unlike the attitude toward poison gases, which would probably be employed only as a retaliatory weapon in response to a gas attack by the other side, the military chiefs of major nations consider that psychochemical warfare is a more humane way to fight a war. These "incapacitating agents" are supposed to disable only temporarily and not be directly lethal. Factories, communications and transportation remain intact, and the people presumably are capable of operating them the day after an attack. Instead of acquiring a destitute, hungry, disease-ridden area, the populace, their homes and industries will be available immediately to support the occupying force's military effort.

Five years ago General Stubbs made the following statement to the Subcommittee on Science and Astronautics of the House of Representatives: "We are attempting to completely separate the incapacitating agents from the lethal agents so that any castigation normally given to toxic agents will not be associated with them, since they do not maim or kill. As a result we hope to have a weapon which will give the commander much freer rein in its use as compared to the toxic agents. It is my hope that through the use of incapacitating agents the free world will have a relatively clear and rapid means of both fighting and deterring limited war which has come to the forefront in the international political scene in the last several years. It is one means by which we can maintain some degree of equality in the face of the overwhelming manpower superiority of the Communist-dominated nations." [1]

A review of the advantages of LSD as an incapacitating agent will help understanding of the interest of the military in this esoteric chemical. It can be cheaply and easily made. Its enormous potency would be an important factor in wartime use. A saboteur could carry enough in an overcoat pocket to produce serious, temporary effects on all the inhabitants of a megapolis if only he could distribute it equally. The contents of a two-suiter piece of luggage will hold an amount sufficient to disable every person in the United States. It is quite soluble in water and only slowly loses its activity in chlorinated water supplies. A short period of boiling does not destroy LSD in solution. Detection is extremely difficult because it is tasteless, odorless and colorless. The inhalation of particles suspended in the air is equally effective as a casualty producer. No doubt food upon which LSD spray has fallen will remain contaminated for days, although the substance could be removed by thorough washing with pure water. The intact skin will not be penetrated, but if some of the material is deposited on the fingers, their brief contact with the mouth may be sufficient to transmit an effective dose.

The city exposed to a successful LSD attack presumably will cease to function. The inhabitants will be so bemused with the odd things that are happening to them and their neighbors that for half a day an aggres-

sor force could take over without substantial resistance.
According to the news releases, by dawn of the next day
everyone will be fit to work under the new management.
Hopefully, the earlier, unsophisticated view has been
abandoned by those concerned with strategic planning.
It is not that simple.

How accurate is General Creasy's expectation that
with psychochemicals "For the first time in history there
is the promise—even the probability—that war will not
necessarily mean death"?[2] Let us try to envision a surprise attack utilizing LSD upon a city to disrupt its
production or in preparation for an airborne assault.
Calculated amounts have been sprayed from an offshore
submarine, and prevailing winds carry the drug across
the population center. A small plane has dropped pack-
ages into the water supplies. Air-defense installations get
special treatment from aerosols released outside their
defensive perimeters by special agents of the enemy.
This multiple attack is superfluous, but even so not
everyone will be directly affected by the drug. Some of
the inhabitants will receive an enormous dose, and some
none at all. Much depends on the quantity released and
the success of dissemination, with the payoff being the
amount delivered into each person's mouth and nose.
Urban populations spend relatively little of their time
outdoors, so that a partial protection from LSD mist is
built into city life. If it settles out of the atmosphere
quickly and does not pass through air-conditioning systems, its effectiveness will be far from complete.

If the amount placed in the water supply makes it
necessary for a man to drink a pint of tap water before

he is affected, not everyone would be involved. Milk, beer, soda pop and one-cup-of-coffee drinkers will not come under its influence immediately. However, the contamination may be so heavy that a person who only brushes his teeth or washes his face will become intoxicated. If the concentration is as high as that, then the infant's formula and the cup of tea become dangerous poisons and talk about a humane war is deceptive. Even assuming that a quantity of LSD not sufficient to cause death except in the very ill or the very susceptible were spread about, and only 10 per cent of the inhabitants came to be directly involved, a large number of fatalities would result. The devastating effects of LSD on people unaware that a chemical is the cause of their mental distortions is enormous and hardly calculable. Those exposed to very minute amounts might be able to fight off the symptoms or attribute their discomfort and that of their neighbors to a new kind of virus. The mildly and moderately intoxicated will be a particular hazard. They will go about feeling somewhat indisposed, but unaware that their judgment, motor skills and performance are impaired. Should some unexposed person attempt to point out their incompetence, they will be prone to lose emotional control and behave aggressively.

One film has been released showing troops who had been exposed to one of the hallucinogens without their knowledge. They were quite unaware of their abnormal state. They could not follow simple commands or perform ordinary tasks with an acceptable degree of accuracy. The sergeant who didn't like coffee continued to behave as usual, but the squad was a shambles. Following the coffee break, two of the enlisted men couldn't stop laughing and broke out into helpless giggling during the remainder of the afternoon. The rest of the men were just as ineffective for combat. They tried to carry out the perplexed sergeant's orders, but discipline and precision vanished. The situation was reminiscent of a slapstick comedy, a military farce which could have been called "The Day the Soldiers Couldn't Stop Laughing."

When larger amounts of LSD are absorbed, many persons will be convinced that they are losing their minds and will become panic-stricken. The effects of the sudden appearance of large numbers of dazed, terrified people in the streets, in vehicles and in workshops can hardly be predicted. Suicides, perhaps homicides, will occur. The accident rate will soar. Even if the air and rail-traffic controllers alone were affected, collisions and secondary fires would be widespread.

The traffic and communications-net breakdown will compound the disaster. Those untouched by the drug will suffer along with the temporarily insane. Caught up in the confusion of a city strangely unbalanced, some of the unexposed might also break down. More than a few of the temporarily deranged will be thrown into a longer-lasting psychosis. The hospitalized psychotics will come off best under the conditions of a psychochemical attack. They are relatively resistant to these agents, and even if affected, the new symptoms will be attributed to their disease process. Furthermore, they will be protected from the newly mad by the same fences that had been built for the protection of the community. It is doubtful that many of the exposed inhabitants will have a psychedelic type of experience; the conditions will not be conducive to a transcendent, blissful interlude. Even if a few did experience a pleasurable state, they will be just as ineffective as the others. The prevailing notion that the populace will fall into a pleasant dream state is untenable. When a large dose of LSD is combined with serious stress, a psychotic reaction will result.

A few hours after the strange epidemic of madness has befallen the city, it will be recognized and identified for what it is by the authorities. Attempts to explain the situation to the people in order to reassure the victims and their families will be made. By this time the hospitals, mortuaries and jails are overfilled. Traffic is chaotic, and the public services are in abeyance. Someone is running amok and must be overpowered. Small bands of the crazed victims have joined to protect themselves from the police. Naked fear is felt by the afflicted and the spared alike.

By nightfall things begin to quiet down. The water supply is still contaminated and will be for days. People refuse to eat any food, even canned goods, afraid that it may be tainted with the poison. Those who may have had a prior LSD exposure will not be much better off than their fellows. This time the reaction will develop in an atmosphere of confusion, doubt and horror. Many are fleeing from "Crazy Town." The suffering will go on for a long time.

We should be aware of two other potential applications of the psychochemicals to military techniques. One is its possible use for interrogation of special prisoners in an effort to break down their ability to resist giving information. Clark reports that Dr. Szent-Gygogyi, President of the University of Szed, stated that the Communists used mescaline for interrogation purposes during the occupation of Hungary after the Second World War. It is difficult to predict how successful the secret administration of LSD would be for this purpose. Probably the captive who can endure physical torture without giving in may be able to avoid informing the enemy even in the midst of a psychotic dissociation. Assuming that he reveals information, the accuracy and reliability of the material would be open to question. The use of the psychotomimetic agents for brainwashing purposes is hardly necessary. Other techniques have proven effective enough.

A further way in which these drugs might conceivably be exploited is their secret administration to one or several of the critical civilian and military decision-makers of a nation. This would not necessarily have the goal of producing disastrous decisions, because the system of checks and counterchecks on crucial judgments tends to neutralize the disturbed thinking of a single man or of a small group. Rather, it might aim at demoralizing the country. Witnessing the mental collapse of the leaders from spaced doses of a psychotomimetic agent would be disheartening. Confidence would be impaired, and those empowered to manage the nation might begin to question the sanity of all their colleagues.

Such degradation of a person's mind is worse than his

physical death and can hardly be considered humane warfare. It is evident that the so-called incapacitating agents are neither nonlethal nor humane. The idea of war seems no more attractive with the mental disruption of LSD than with the ulceration of skin and lung caused by mustard gas.

It is interesting that we accept certain military methods of destruction and reject others. The club, the sword, the spear, the gun and the flame are classically acknowledged devices of annihilation. Their more modern elaborations—the missile, the tank, the bomb and the flame-thrower—are tolerated as legitimate agents of warfare. All of these devices are direct in their action and *visible*. A second type of armament, equally lethal, arouses more distaste and revulsion; these are indirect in their action and *invisible*. Radioactivity is a prime example. The fire-and-blast effects of the atomic bomb caused many more casualties than did radiation, yet it is against radioactivity that the protests are lodged. The reactions to gas and germ warfare are additional examples of the abhorrence in which invisible, insidious methods of killing are held. The psychochemicals belong in this category. In LSD we have not yet discovered a compassionate, nonlethal way to wage war.

Unfortunately the great nations, and some of the lesser ones, are stockpiling the psychochemicals because of fears of what the other side might do. The psychochemicals will be the most difficult of all weaponry to control and supervise if disarmament ever comes. Meanwhile they should be recognized for what they are—agents of war with, not without, death.

12. *Postview*

Our brain seems to be evolving in the direction of an increasing dampening or inhibition of sensory input. Inhibitory activity of the nervous system is essential to analyze what is going on and to keep oriented to the immediate situation. If the mass of unessential information coming into the brain was not "quenched"—that is, inhibited—the bulk of sensory data would quickly overwhelm our sorting and evaluating capacity. Overloading the system is avoided by quenching most of the incoming sensations. Life, limb and sanity are preserved by the discriminate rejection and sorting of sensory experience.

Much is gained by this process, but what is lost? As the brain rejects, reduces, averages or evaluates the percept, it is lost, dimmed, made ordinary or subordinated to its symbolic concept. LSD may temporarily and selectively disinhibit the brain's inhibitory activity. Some, but not all, of the observed LSD phenomena could be accounted for by a disinhibitory effect of the drug.

The waking, sane state can be thought of as an inhibitor of a more primal, fantasy, dreamlike condition which re-emerges when vigilance is reduced, as in sleep, with LSD or on certain other occasions. In this primal psychological state underlying rational consciousness the boundaries of the self are diffused, and the learned, imposed meanings of objects are altered to a point where objects have no significance except for themselves. Colors become, by loss of inhibitory influence, more saturated and brilliant, and the viewed object is seen in its primary form unencumbered by utilitarian values.

The capacity to perform the arithmetic of life suffers. In its place a thinking-feeling metaphoric imagery emerges. Unfamiliar, unconventional, multifaceted thought sequences flow past, or a single, timeless theme reverberates endlessly. The feeling tone, also liberated from the restraints generally imposed by ordinary wakefulness, is less restricted and more unstable. The check reins placed upon the nervous system to keep each sensory channel and each mental process distinct and intact are loosened. Sound permeates sight, feeling interweaves with thinking, and both become joined with perceiving.

Reality orientation, goal direction and adaptation to the environment are all partially or totally impaired, and the usual state of mental inhibition called sanity is disinhibited. Whether insanity or what has been named unsanity emerges depends upon the emotional acceptance of this defenseless, egoless, prelogical, highly suggestible condition. Strong feelings of insecurity and anxiety lead to a failure to compose and organize the unusual experience; this is insanity. Emotional acceptance leads to its composition and to unsanity. Even in the unsane condition attention can be focused: inward for a new look at the old problems, outward for a new vision of the old world.

The varieties of LSD experience are many. LSD has mimicked almost every sort of acute psychotic response, and the spectrum of visionary states has been fairly well duplicated. From the broad array each observer manages to derive material which validates his own doctrine. There are also other aspects: purely philosophical introspections, visual feasts, sensual raptures and encounters more elemental than any of these.

It is tempting to say that one gets from the LSD encounter what one deserves, but this is not so. Seven centuries ago St. Thomas Aquinas said it more accurately: *"Quid quid recipiteur secundum modum recipientis recipiteur"*: "Whatever is received is received according to the nature of the recipient." We get, not what we deserve, but what we are. A pill does not construct character, educate the emotions or improve intelligence. It is not a spiritual labor-saving device, salvation, instant wisdom, or a short cut to maturity. However, it can be an opportunity to experience oneself and the world in a new way—and to learn from it.

From the profusion of the known response patterns and of others which may still be unexplored, it is obvious that LSD does nothing specific. It springs the latch of disinhibition. What emerges depends upon what was within and upon all the impinging influences from without. These speculations on the mode of action of LSD will require much more work before their accuracy can be confirmed or disproven.

What the future holds for LSD and the other members of this group can hardly be predicted from an analysis of the present situation. Its precise role as an adjunct to psychotherapy is not established. However, a number of excellent psychiatrists, particularly in Europe, are reporting favorable results with LSD and psilocybin. More psychiatrists may, in time to come, accept the value of a drug-induced sudden transforming encounter. It is agreed that short-term therapy with LSD is a "superego cure" and that it changes only the attitudes and values of the patient. It is a limited goal, to be sure, but gratifying to those who need it.

As a laboratory aid to the study of both the abnormal and normal activities of the mind the hallucinogens offer great promise. Biochemists, neurophysiologists and electroencephalographers are employing the hallucinogens as one tool in the development of a basic science of psychiatry. The distortions of the psychotic can be grossly approximated with these drugs. The objective measurement of anomalous mental activity will be helpful indeed. The ability to subjectively experience the state is a learning experience for workers with the mentally disturbed. One day the hallucinogens may also help answer questions about artistic creativity and scientific inspiration by clarifying how ideational associations and symbols are formed.

It is urgent that we obtain information about the infrastructure of the mind, and relatively soon. We must somehow learn more about our drives, impulses and emotions—this part of the mind must come to be understood by the reasoning part. We must know more about what we are like and whether anything can be done about it.

The nature of some LSD experiences brings the scientist into a confrontation with the neurochemical substrata of faith. Uncritical belief, total acceptance and nonrational conviction are intrinsic properties of human belief systems. Their study will be most rewarding.

The mysticomimetic component of the LSD state will give the student of mysticism a laboratory device for its controlled production. There is much to learn about what we call "ego dissolution" and the mystics call "self-transcendence," what we call "regression" and they call "mystical union," what we subsume under "withdrawal" and they call "renunciation of the illusion of reality."

It is interesting that the mystics who achieve their state through drugs are less hopeful that the condition can be a proper subject for scientific study than those who enter it by spiritual exercises. The users of mysticomimetic compounds generally claim that the experience can never be scientifically examined. On the other hand, the "natural" mystics are more open to the possibility. U. A. Asrami, Professor of Physics at Benares University and a well-known mystic, says in his *Synthesis of Science and Mysticism,* "The modern techniques of scientific research could be helpful in determining the limitations, the after effects and the utility of the mystical experience. It seems to me that the time has come when a study of this kind becomes imperative. . . . If mysticism and mystical experience can be freed of their 'supernatural' connotations, there is no reason why modern science cannot acknowledge and even absorb them into its domain. If the religious man will, on his side, submit to a scientific definition of mystical experience, there is nothing to prevent the building of a bridge between science and mysticism." [1]

The possibility that these avenues of inquiry will not be explored for a long time is real. Let the hallucinogens become popular items of underworld commerce, let them become the tipple of those seeking novelty and excitement, then the community reacts excessively and prohibitive laws follow. The investigator becomes unwilling or unable to work under these conditions. At a recent conference on addiction there was a movement to classify LSD and similar drugs as narcotics. They are not narcotics, but the fears provoked by their unconsidered use is forcing the law-enforcement agencies to recommend new and highly restrictive legislation.

For the first time members of highly developed urban cultures can reliably achieve a chemically induced unsanity—a condition which till now has been the privilege of the shaman, the visionary and a few others including the peyote and mushroom congregations. It is true that there are many hashish habitués, but most of them belong to backward cultures or are found on the periphery of modern communities. The question has been raised whether hashish has kept the Middle and Near East backward, poverty-stricken and without the will to better themselves. This is very doubtful. Greater forces than the use of Indian hemp have produced the passivity and lack of development of these societies.

What is a rationalistic, materialistic, rather nonbelieving society to do with the visionary drugs? Should they be totally prohibited? Who should have access to them— the scientist doing research? the psychotherapist? the philosopher who wants to explore his mental processes? the artist who hopes for an enhanced creativity? the mystic? the hedonist?

Let us immediately discard the notion that there are "good" and "bad" drugs. Opium is "bad" when smoked in a filthy den while one's children starve at home. It is "good" when used skillfully to relieve pain. Marihuana was a "good" drug when it was taken by Asian mystics to assist in their meditations; it was "bad" as it was used by the Assassins. The Christian and the yogin ethic agree that a thing has no intrinsic good or evil in it, but the manner of usage determines the evaluation to be placed on it. So, too, the psychedelics are neither "good" nor "bad" drugs; they have "good" and "bad" usages. They have provided us with important information about the mind (good) ; reports of prolonged breakdowns following their use are available (bad) . Some patients have improved their pernicious behavior patterns (good) ; they are being sold to juveniles on the black market (bad) .

The bad use of the hallucinogens is nothing new. Even the divine mushroom has led to disaster, according to Duran. After the human sacrifices that celebrated the coronation of Montezuma II in 1502 had been completed, the populace ate specially gathered mushrooms. Many committed suicide at the height of the bemushroomed state; others received visions and were able to prophesy the future.

It is in the context of encouraging the good uses and discouraging the bad uses of such drugs as LSD that legislation should be enacted. Neither a complete prohibition or a complete lack of protective regulations would be appropriate.

We are hurtling up the steep slope of the ascending curve of progress. Every index, whether it be the speed of travel, the effectiveness of communication devices, the number of scientific discoveries, the growth of populations or the destructiveness of armaments, is accelerating at an extraordinary pace. We speak of a population explosion; it is just as proper to speak of a scientific explosion, an information explosion, transportation, communication and armament explosions, and many others. Social change is so rapid that the precepts of one generation become the absurdities of the next. The lack of stability, the loss of the traditional securities and the mounting complexity of living are psychologically distressing. Furthermore, the aspirations of the age seem impermanent and superficial. The eternal questions of how to live and how to die are answered no more satisfactorily than during the Dark Ages.

The hallucinogens are a fragment of the current predicament. They represent an escape from frustrating existence for some. Others are sustained by the crystalline look at themselves and their world seen during that endless moment. And a few marvel at the vastness within.

Appendix A

The Chemistry of the Hallucinogens

Most of the hallucinogens contain an indole structure:

THE INDOLE RING

Not all indoles are hallucinogenic. Some are necessary constituents of our diet, like the ubiquitous amino acid, tryptophane. A derivative of tryptophane is serotonin (5-hydroxytryptamine). Only about 1 per cent of the ingested tryptophane is converted to serotonin, but that 1 per cent is vital for the transmission of nerve impulses, blood coagulation and many other body functions.

TRYPTOPHANE   SEROTONIN

Since serotonin is a normal, necessary chemical transmitter of impulses across synapses (the connections
between nerve cells), it is intriguing to find that certain
hallucinogens have chemical structures very similar to
serotonin.

Bufotenine, a constituent of the *Amanita muscarina*
mushroom, and dimethyltryptamine (DMT), found in
cohaba snuff, are examples of the minimal chemical
alteration required to change a vital neurochemical into
a psychotomimetic compound.

$$HO - \underset{\underset{H}{N}}{\text{indole}} - CH_2 \cdot CH_2 \cdot N \underset{CH_3}{\overset{CH_3}{<}}$$

BUFOTENINE

$$\underset{\underset{H}{N}}{\text{indole}} - CH_2 \cdot CH_2 \cdot N \underset{CH_3}{\overset{CH_3}{<}}$$

DMT

When the close structural relationship between serotonin and the hallucinogens was discovered, the specula-
tion arose that the chemically produced psychoses, and
perhaps even naturally occurring ones like schizophrenia, were due to serotonin antagonism. Most of the
psychotomimetics were found to have an antiserotonin
action. It was considered likely that they competed at
the synapse with serotonin, and if sufficient or crucial
synapses were occupied by the hallucinogen, disturbed
thinking would result. Such a simple explanation of

psychosis is untenable. Many indolic compounds with high antiserotonin activity known to penetrate into the brain cell do not produce the psychotomimetic state. Conversely, we now know of psychotomimetics which have no serotonin antagonism whatsoever.

The active components of the Aztec psilocybe mushroom, psilocybin and psilocin, are also structurally reminiscent of serotonin.

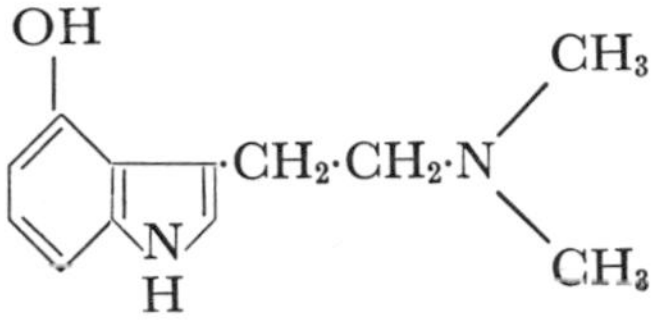

PSILOCIN

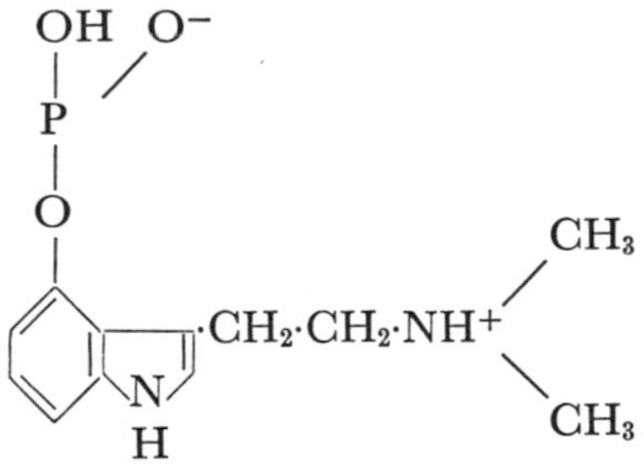

PSILOCYBIN

Psilocybin breaks down to psilocin in the body by splitting off the phosphoric acid group. Psilocybin is 200 times weaker than LSD by weight.

Lysergic acid diethylamide, or more properly d-lysergic acid diethylamide tartarate, is also called LSD-25 and Delysid. The "LSD" part of the abbreviation is from the German, LysergSäure Diethylamid. The "25" indicates that it was the 25th in a series of analogous compounds synthesized in the Sandoz laboratories. By common usage it has been shortened to LSD. It is often called lysergic acid, but this is actually the name of an antecedent compound which has no psychotomimetic properties.

The chemical structure of LSD looks formidable, but it is indolic, and has the same $CH_2 \cdot CH_2 \cdot N \Big\langle {}^{CH_3}_{CH_3}$ "tail" as psilocin, DMT and other hallucinogens. It also has an

LSD-25

LSD-25 DRAWN TO SHOW
THE SIMILARITY TO DMT

attachment at the same point of the indole nucleus as psilocin (the 4 position).

A long series of lysergic acid derivatives have been made, some are completely inactive, others approach, but never exceed, LSD in potency. The slightest change in chemical structure may result in a profound loss of activity. LSD turns a beam of polarized light to the right; the mirror-image compound, the form which turns a light beam to the left, is without any psychic action whatever. If a single bromine atom is added to LSD at the 1 position, a compound without psychic effects but with more antiserotonin activity is produced.

The morning glory seeds (ololiuqui) contain lysergic acid amide and isolysergic acid amide, weaker members of the LSD group.

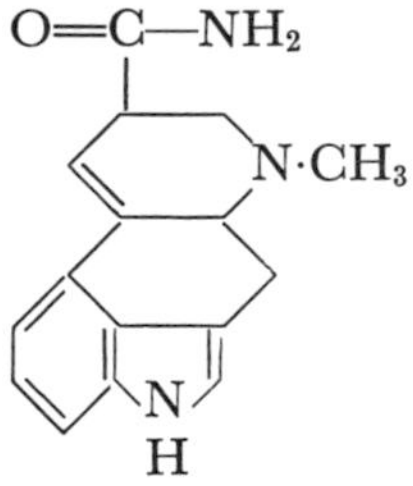

LYSERGIC ACID AMIDE

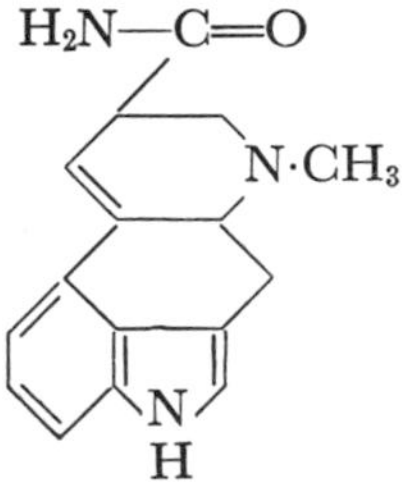

ISOLYSERGIC ACID AMIDE

The chemical structure of ibogaine, the active alkaloid of the Congolese ordeal plant, *iboga tabernanthe,* is
known. It is related to harmine, found in the South
American banisteria vine. They both contain the indole
ring structure.

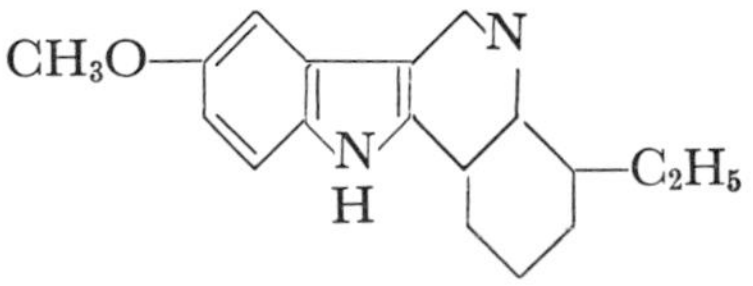

CH$_3$O— N

N
H —C$_2$H$_5$

IBOGAINE

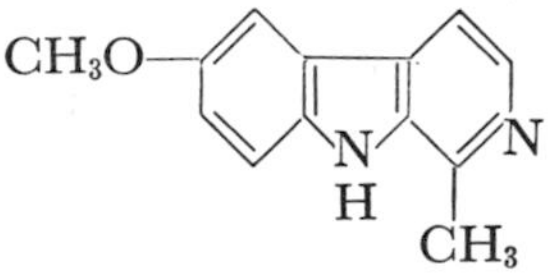

CH$_3$O— N

N
H CH$_3$

HARMINE

Of all the naturally occurring hallucinogens only the
cannabinols, the active principles from hashish, are not
indolic or potential indoles. Why their spatial arrange-
ment should result in a mental state resembling the
hallucinogenic indoles is unknown.

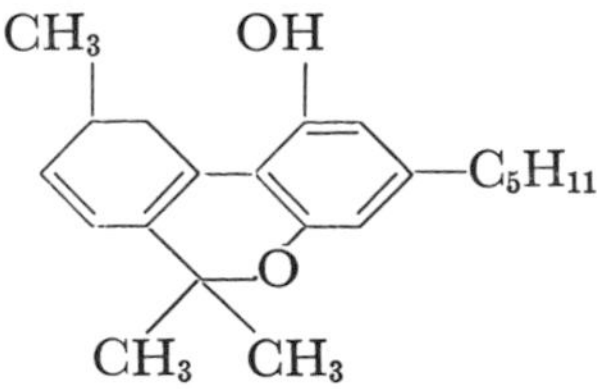

CH$_3$ OH

—C$_5$H$_{11}$

O
CH$_3$ CH$_3$

TETRAHYDROCANNABINOL

Mescaline, the most active of the peyote cactus alkaloids, is not an indole but has been described as a

potential indole, meaning that the "tail" might be joined into a ring after it is absorbed in the body. Actually this is unlikely, since its excretion product is also not indolic. It is 4,000 times weaker than LSD by weight.

$$CH_3O—\underset{OCH_3}{\bigcirc}—\underset{\underset{N\ H_2}{CH_2}}{CH_2} \rightarrow CH_3O—\underset{OCH_3}{\bigcirc}—\underset{COOH}{CH_2}$$

MESCALINE   EXCRETION PRODUCT
                   OF MESCALINE

$$CH_3O—\underset{CH_3O}{\bigcirc}—\underset{\underset{N\ H_2}{CH_2}}{CH_2}$$

THIS INACTIVE PRODUCT
WAS RECENTLY FOUND IN THE
URINE OF SCHIZOPHRENICS,
NOT IN NORMALS

Mescaline has certain similarities in chemical configuration to adrenalin, another transmitter of signals across nerve cells. Hoffer and Osmond have postulated that schizophrenia may result from the abnormal breakdown

$$HO—\underset{HO}{\bigcirc}—\underset{\underset{NH}{\underset{CH_3}{|}}}{CHOH} \longrightarrow HO—\underset{HO}{\bigcirc}—\underset{\underset{CH_3}{N}}{CHOH}$$

ADRENALIN   ADRENOLUTIN

of adrenalin to a compound like adrenolutin. They believe that this deviant pathway in adrenalin metabolism might be genetically determined or might result from excessive and prolonged anxiety.

It has been mentioned that atropine from belladonna leaves and scopolamine from henbane are deliriant in excessive doses. Their medical uses are as anticholinergics—that is, they counteract the effects of acetylcholine. Acetylcholine happens to be the third (in addition to serotonin and adrenalin) of the cerebral neural transmitters.

Anticholinergics have a large number of useful functions in medicine. They are called antispasmodics when used to relax the muscles of the intestine and stomach. They reduce the flow of stomach acid in peptic ulcer patients. They dilate the pupil for eye examinations. They are given before surgery to dry up the flow of saliva and other mucous secretions. In earlier days they were used as remedies for asthmatic attacks but have been superseded by better medications. A recent increase in the sales of Asthmador, an ancient patent medicine composed of belladonna and stramonium (Jimson weed) is due to purchases by members of the beatnik microculture. When it is taken in larger than recommended amounts, a delirium is induced. This recalls the strange incident almost 300 years ago when a platoon of Redcoats responded to Governor Berkeley's alarm to put down the rebellion of Nathaniel Bacon. They bivouacked near Jamestown, Virginia, and gathered wild greens for a stew. The Indians could have warned the Englishmen against James Town (later Jimson) weed, for it was well known to them as a deliriant used to initiate the young braves into the rites of manhood. Beverly describes the odd events as follows:

> The James-Town Weed is supposed to be one of the greatest Coolers in the World. This being an early plant, it was gathered very young for a boiled salad by some of the Soldiers sent thither to pacify the Troubles of Bacon; and some of them did eat plentifully of it, the Effect of which was a very pleasant Comedy; for they turned natural Fools for several Days. One would blow up a Feather in the Air. Another would dart straws at it with much Fury. Another, stark naked, was sitting in a Corner like a Monkey, grinning and making Mows at them. A Fourth would fondly kiss and paw his Companions, and sneer in their Faces with a Countenance more antick than any in a Dutch Droll. In this frantik Condition they were confined, lest they should in their Folly destroy themselves; though it was observed that all their Actions were full of Innocence and good Nature. Indeed, they were not very cleanly; for they would have wallowed in their own Excrements if they had not been prevented. A Thousand such simple Tricks they played, and after Eleven Days returned to themselves again not remembering anything that had passed.

A series of new anticholinergics have been synthesized during the past decade which mimic the mental symptoms of the hallucinogens and result in less mental confusion than the deliriants. It well may be that the

visual and ideational alterations result from an inter-
ference with acetyl choline activity in the brain. It is
currently considered possible that these drugs blockade
incoming sensory information and act as a sort of
chemical sensory deprivation. When this group of drugs
are combined with the sensory deprivation condition,
their effects are diminished.

They are not indoles, as can be seen from the formulas
of two of the better-known psychotomimetic anticholinergics.

DITRAN

SERNYL

Both Ditran and Sernyl are likely to evoke unpleasant
side effects including incoordination, visual difficulties,
dry mouth, flushing and palpitation. In one instance the
former drug produced a complete loss of insight and
amnesia for more than a day after an average dose had
been given.

The earlier belief that hallucinogens had to be indoles
is unwarranted. In order to fit the indole theory, it was

hypothesized that mescaline was converted to an indole in the body, although meager positive evidence was at hand. The cannabinol configuration tended to be ignored. With a lengthening series of such synthetic compounds as Ditran and Sernyl issuing from the biochemical laboratories, it is obvious that a wide variety of nonindolic chemical forms can give rise to the state called hallucinogenic.

Appendix B

Table 1

A COMPARISON OF THE LSD AND SENSORY-DEPRIVATION STATES

	LSD	SENSORY DEPRI-VATION
I. PERCEPTION		
Intensification of color and depth	+	+
Visual illusions	+	+
Visual pseudohallucinations	+	+
Visual hallucinations	+	+
Persistence of the after image	+	+
Hyperacusis	+	+
Auditory hallucinations	rare	+
Hallucinations of touch, smell and taste	rare	+
II. AFFECT		
Euphoria	+	rare
Anxiety	+	+
Emotional instability	+	+
Inappropriateness	+	+

Table 1—Continued

III. BODY IMAGE CHANGES

Depersonalization	+	+
Derealization	+	+

IV. IDEATION

Fantasy imagery	+	+
Flight of ideas	+	+
Ideas of reference	+	+
Delusions	+	+
Impairment of concentration	+	+
Impaired intelligence testing	+	+

V. ORIENTATION

Impaired for time	+	+
Impaired for place	rare	rare

VI. MOTOR COORDINATION

Impaired on testing	+	+

Table 2

CHANGES IN	MODEL PSYCHOSIS PRODUCED BY LSD	ACUTE CATATONIC EXCITEMENT (SCHIZO-PHRENIC REACTION)	ACUTE DELIRIUM (TOXIC PSYCHOSIS)
1. PERCEPTION	Illusions, frequent intensified visual perception. Pseudohallucinations. Hallucinations, mainly visual. Other sensory hallucinations are rare.	Illusions, rarely intensified perceptions. Hallucinations, mainly auditory but also visual. Other sensory hallucinations are rare.	Illusions. Hallucinations, mainly visual. Other sensory hallucinations are rare.
2. COGNITION	Impairment of judgment and abstract reasoning for practical problem-solving purposes. Blocking. Ideas of reference. Delusions. Disorganized ideation.	Marked impairment of judgment and abstract reasoning. Blocking, use of metaphor. Ideas of reference. Bizarre delusions. Disorganized ideation.	Impairment of judgment, memory, orientation and abstract reasoning. Ideas of reference. Delusions are less bizarre, more "homey" confabulation.
3. AFFECT	Anxiety, depression, or elation, ecstasy. Uncontrollable laughter or tears.	Anxiety, terror. Rarely euphoria or ecstasy. Mutism, inappropriate moods, stupor.	Anxiety, fearfulness, perplexity. Rarely euphoria.
4. BEHAVIOR	Passive, rarely restless, and overactive.	Gesturing, grimacing, destructive, withdrawn, automatism, negativism, hostility.	Agitated, apprehensive, restless, stuporous, hyperactive.
5. POSTURE	Slight tremor. Slight unsteadiness.	Complete immobility. Pacing. "caged animal." Posturing.	Tremulous. Picking movements. Unsteady gait, ataxia.
6. CONSCIOUSNESS	Relatively clear	Relatively clear but preoccupied.	Clouded, confused. Fluctuating from hour to hour.
7. REALITY TESTING	Slightly or moderately impaired.	Greatly impaired.	Greatly impaired.
8. SPEECH	Blocking, halting, sometimes unimpaired.	Condensations, alliterations, blocking, echolalia, clang associations.	Slurred, blocking.
9. EGO BOUNDARIES	Depersonalization. Derealization.	Depersonalization. Derealization.	Depersonalization.

Table 3

	ACUTE SCHIZOPHRENIA (ACUTE CATATONIC EXCITEMENT)	THE VISIONARY STATE (SPONTANEOUS TYPE)	THE INSPIRATION (THE UNIFYING IDEA)
1. PREDISPOSING FACTORS	Frustration, insecurity, guilt, anxiety, etc., in a predisposed individual.	Frustration, insecurity, intense emotion, etc., in a predisposed individual.	Acquisition of necessary background information and experience which are necessary for eventual problem solving. In instances of artistic inspiration the technical ability must be available (preparation).
2. LATENT PERIOD	Gradual mobilization of available defenses to maintain acceptable interpersonal relationships. These are inadequate and crumble.	Intellectual and psychological efforts at personal problem solving culminating in periods of physical and mental exhaustion.	Conscious striving to solve the scientific or artistic problem has been fruitless. It is set aside and attention is turned to other matters (incubation).
3. THE IDEA	The sudden delusional projection of the conflict ("I am God"). Emotional discharge as ecstasy, furor, depression, stupor.	The revelation, the Light. Emotional discharge as exaltation.	The inspiration, a subliminal problem-solving process with only the final solution springing to consciousness. Emotional discharge as elation (illumination).
4. DEVELOPMENTAL PERIOD	Further paranoid elaboration of the central delusion.	Reshuffling of ego defenses (sudden personality change). Restructuring old patterns of behavior.	Elaboration of the central idea, critical inspection with modifications (elaboration).
5. FINAL RESULT	(a) Re-establishment of the prepsychotic level of ego function. (b) Chronicity, flattening, increased mental disorganization (chronic schizophrenia).	(a) Return to old patterns of living. (b) Continuing personal and group change in a direction of greater effectiveness (cults, religions, movements).	(a) Discarding the idea. (b) Final polishing, new applications, testing of validity or value by others (verification).

References

Chapter II

1. Hofmann, A., "Chemical Pharmacology and Medical Aspects of Psychotomimetics," *Journal of Experimental Medical Sciences,* Vol. V, 1961, p. 31.
2. Hensley, A., Letter to the Commissioner of Indian Affairs, U.S. Bureau of Indian Affairs, File #2989—1908—126.3.
3. Stoll, W. A., "LSD-25, A Hallucinatory Agent of the Ergot Group," *Swiss Archives of Neurology,* Vol. 60, 1947, p. 279.

Chapter III

1. Behringer, K., *Der Meskalinrausch,* Berlin, Julius Springer, 1926.
2. Kast, E. C., "LSD Used as an Analgesic," *Journal of the American Medical Association,* Vol. 187, January 4, 1964, p. 33.

Chapter IV

1. Brain, W. R., *Disturbances of the Nervous System,* New York, Oxford University Press, 1951.

Chapter V

1. Benedict, R., *Patterns of Culture*, Boston, Houghton-Mifflin, 1934.
2. Hennell, T., *Witnesses: The Experiences of a Mental Patient*, Philadelphia, W. B. Saunders, 1938.
3. Sechehaye, M., *Autobiography of a Schizophrenic Girl*, New York, Grune & Stratton, 1951.

Chapter VI

1. McDonald, N., "Living with Schizophrenia," *Canadian Medical Association Journal*, Vol. 82, January 23, 1960, p. 218.
2. Huxley, A., *Heaven and Hell*, New York, Harper & Row, 1956.

Chapter IX

1. Marmor, J., "Psychoanalytic Therapy as an Educational Process," paper read at the annual meeting of the Academy of Psychoanalysis, Chicago, May, 1961.

Chapter XI

1. Lieberman, E. J., "Psychochemicals as Weapons," *Bulletin of Atomic Scientists*, January, 1962.
2. *Ibid.*

Chapter XII

1. Asrami, U. A., "Synthesis of Science and Mysticism," *Main Currents in Modern Thought*, Vol. 20, September–October, 1963.

Index

Dr. Sidney Cohen

Born in New York City in 1910, Dr. Sidney Cohen became a doctor of medicine at Bonn University in Germany and received his Ph.D. from Columbia University in New York. He is Chief of Psychosomatic Medicine at the Veterans Administration Hospital in Los Angeles, Associate Clinical Professor of Medicine at the University of California and editor of *Mind: Psychiatry in General Practice*. The author of *Psychochemotherapy: The Physician's Manual,* published in 1962, Dr. Cohen has extended his research activities into all classes of drugs which affect the mind. Over seventy articles reporting these findings have been published in scientific journals. For ten years he has investigated many problems of LSD and the other hallucinogens and has contributed some of the basic information in this field. His work has been a source of material for many of the popular reports on LSD. They cite his researches on the therapeutic use, side effects and complications, and his descriptions of the various hallucinogenic states from the psychotic to the transcendental. His researches with LSD, on which he has lectured both here and abroad, are currently directed toward measuring the changes of values, attitudes and originality. Dr. Cohen lives in Los Angeles.